Nov 21st

Emm.

●●●●●●●●●●●●●●●●●●●●●●●●●●●●●●

BITING THE Beanbag

Everywoman's Rather Rude and Frightfully Frank ABC of Pregnancy

A Funny and Biased Guide Written by a
Mother of Three Children Under Four

JILL PARKIN

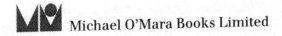 Michael O'Mara Books Limited

First published in Great Britain in 1997 by
Michael O'Mara Books Limited
9 Lion Yard, Tremadoc Road
London SW4 7NQ

A CIP catalogue record for this book is available from the British Library

ISBN 1-85479-238-5

Designed and typeset by Martin Bristow
Printed and bound by Cox & Wyman, Reading, Berkshire

For David

Introduction

Listen. You can't trust your mother or your friend to tell you the truth about having babies, and your partner won't have a clue even if he's fathered a complete football team over the years. There's an ages-old conspiracy to clean it up, talc it down and keep it quiet. The fear is that if you knew what it was really like, you'd buy a cat or a DIY vasectomy kit on the spot. You wouldn't actually. Though you might scour the market for a test-tube in nine-month size.

They'll be delighted when you tell them the news. They'll be impressed by the beautiful creature on your scan picture. And they'll send you flowers when the baby is born. But they won't tell you that your navel will pop inside out, that the way you smell will turn your partner on or that your breasts will expand into melons almost overnight.

This book tells you all that and more. Because I've been there – and back – three times in four years.

Okay, not quite back. I don't think I'll ever go back all the way: life is too short to stuff a thrice-stretched woman into a twenty-four-inch waist. This is the pregnancy manual without the mother-and-baby step video. (If you've got time to watch a video after having a baby, make it one you can watch while drinking a glass of wine.) My one regret is that I haven't been able to include a 40H cup with every copy.

It isn't a medical book, fascinated though it is by swellings and gurglings. Nor is it a 'miracle of motherhood' book. It *won't* tell you how many tennis courts an ironed-out placenta would cover, and it won't tell you how centred and strong you will feel during the last trimester. But it *will* tell you the best sort of knickers to buy and why you should avoid washing up while pregnant, which will make you a lot more comfortable than the other two bits of information.

It is rather rude and frightfully frank, as the cover says and as our mothers aren't. Only when the baby has arrived do they start talking about their own experience, bit by bit and a lot too late. This is an age where many of us reach childbirth without coming across masses of pregnant women or cuddling lots of babies. We turn to our mothers for knowledge long after their own feet-swellin', bladder-burstin', fancy-a-chip-dunked-in jam days are over. They glimpse a possibility of grandchildren, smile sweetly and affect amnesia.

So, I hope this book is the truth, the whole truth and a good giggle. Whatever happens to you during pregnancy has happened to other women, however uniquely odd or painful or hilarious it may seem.

It's just that no told you about it. Until now.

Jill Parkin

Active birth

Actually, the nearest most of us come to this is picking up the books about it. But I like the idea, don't you? Woman in charge. Put your left leg round the back of your neck, if this helps. Taking care not to knock your acupuncture needle out, of course. Sing, bawl, do your own thing. Stroll around the garden, bake a cake or light scented candles. Aromatherapist on call. New Age music on CD player. Wouldn't it be good?

The truth is there's only one person in charge here. And that's the baby – single-minded, utterly ruthless and ready to come out. The rest of us are fooling ourselves.

After a first delivery lying on a bed attached to a ridiculous amount of machinery, I did better second time round and managed a beanbag birth. Very trendy this and in all the active birth books. Great position, but active? Once down there, I stayed down there, unable even to take off my jersey, which remained round my neck with one sleeve on and one off throughout.

My third delivery, at home, was remarkably active – largely because I didn't realize it was about to happen. I baked rock cakes, made up a bed, bathed the two children and then thought: this backache feels familiar. Baby arrived shortly afterwards and just a few minutes after the midwife.

Whole books have been written about this active birth business, chapter after chapter devoted to telling you that squatting is the way to open your pelvis and let the baby through. All true, but it's not so much activity as gravity which counts. Even so, don't expect baby to descend like Newton's apple. More like a melon. Through a tight sock.

Age

The average age for having a first baby is twenty-eight these days. Tell that to your mother-in-law when she starts getting out of hand and talking about 'leaving it late'. Consultants start showing concern when you're around thirty-six. Their secretaries ring up and ask you along for 'a chat with Mr Knows-Best'. He runs through the tests available for screening out deformities and puts more or less pressure on you, depending on your age, his age and how willing you are to be lectured. Worth listening, worth getting the facts, then you can make your own mind up later. After all, you're old enough. As your mother-in-law will tell you.

Of course, if men had the babies, by now the tests would be safer for the babies, less harrowing for the pregnant people, available much earlier in the pregnancy and far more accurate. And very probably unnecessary, because the race would be dying out anyway.

Under 20 – This is too young. Your pelvic bones are too soft and your boyfriend is only a child himself. Dancing around your handbag is one thing. Dancing around your nappy bag is quite another. Get yourself a life of your own first.

Around 25 – Think about it. Are you ready for a stomach which rests on your thighs? You have a career ahead of you. You may resent the interruption. Sexual harassment behind the filing cabinet is much harder with a forty-five-inch waist – you just can't get near him.

Around 30 – Is that a biological tick you hear? Or the siren call of the child-free life? Tired of wearing that tight little business suit? Go on, take out a savings plan for your maternity leave and start buying books like this one.

Over 35 – Don't think about it, do it. Before he starts dancing round someone else's handbag.

Over 40 – Preferably now, tonight. And afterwards keep your legs in the air for as long as you can bear it.

His age – You may think it's irrelevant. It used to be said that it was, except for a lessening in sperm production after the age of fifty-five. But now, with a dramatic decrease in the Western sperm count, a vintage man is the best bet. Men born before 1958 and earlier apparently have far more of the required wriggly things.

Alcohol

It helps. I knocked back two large glasses of wine before the easiest birth of the lot. It should be on the methods of pain relief list – gas and air, TENS machine, pethidine, epidural, Chardonnay.

Not that you should tipple too much when you're pregnant. Most women are sensible and follow this well-tried pattern. First pregnancy: no alcohol for three months before attempting conception and none during pregnancy. Second pregnancy: the occasional glass or two after the three-month mark. Third pregnancy: the occasional glass or two throughout, and the odd small gin when pressed. For example: 'I don't suppose you will, will you, darling?' 'I'd better not. Just a small one for me, darling.' Fourth pregnancy? How do you think this keeps happening in the first place?

Alcohol in pregnancy is one of those things the medical gurus keep changing their minds about. Most of them are the wrong sex to get pregnant themselves, and so their advice should be taken with a pinch of salt and the odd glass of what makes you a contented mother-to-be. If you're happy, baby's happy. Keep telling yourself that.

Of course, if you cut it out altogether for nine to twelve months, you've nothing to worry about at all. Except for the fact that it will feel like eighteen to twenty-four months.

Amniotic sac

The water-filled bag surrounding your baby is made up of a double membrane. If it doesn't break in reasonable time during labour, the chances are a midwife or a doctor carrying an outsize crochet hook will come to see you. And it won't be about making a matinée jacket. (See *Waters*)

Antenatal classes

'Now I want you all, pregnant people and partners, to stand around in a horseshoe shape. Good. Could the two ends of the horseshoe just move a leetle closer? Good. Now just imagine that you are a contracting uterus and you two end people are the cervix. . . .'

If you thought pregnancy was natural and nothing to be embarrassed about, let antenatal classes change your mind. And if you thought your husband was going to be with you for the birth, wash your mouth out. He's your partner. Husbands, like wedding rings in baby book pictures, have been abolished by antenatal classes.

'Bring partner and pillow,' I was told. 'Eh?' said my terrified husband. (Yes, I admit it – I'm a married mother.) 'You want me to come? Will there be other men there?' Nothing like antenatal classes for bringing the Old Man out of the New.

Down at the local day centre the three of us – pregnant person, partner and pillow – lay on a carpet dotted with mashed potato from that day's lunch. And we all – men included – exercised as ordered. Partners were exempt from the pelvic floor, if not the potato floor. 'It's good for sex too,' said the midwife as the bumps on the carpet squeezed with clenched knees and crossed eyes. 'What's that?' asked a partner. I remembered a friend who told me that if she did too many pelvic floor exercises she got terribly turned on. 'Well, if that happens, it's just you and your pillow,' muttered husband.

But antenatal classes are supposed to be educational too. Hence the flip charts with an effacing cervix, a dilating cervix and a cervix with a baby's head in it. 'I'll never remember all this,' wailed one woman during my first session. 'I've only got one GCSE.'

'It'll happen whether you remember it or not,' said another. It was her fifth baby, but her husband's first. 'We only came for him. "Go by yourself," I said. But when he rang up they said they liked to see partners, so I've come along too.'

Antenatal classes provide you with a gang of ready-made friends. Great. Prams clash in the street and you peer at what she got. And you coo: 'What a good baby! Who does she look like? And you look really well!' Translates as: 'Looks a bit of a dumpling to me. Wonder if it's all right? A dead ringer for Winston Churchill. God, you've stacked on the weight!' Over the years you'll have guaranteed sympathy (translates as rivalry) about everything from first teeth to first sex from a load of people you once squeezed buttocks with.

Appetite

For food, that is. We do sex later in the book. Some women, as soon as the fertilized egg hits the womb wall, start eating like a horse. Standing up, that is. They stand by the open fridge and eat everything in sight without benefit of plate or fork. Sitting down delays things. So does actually heating anything up.

Partners who really want to give the bump the hump need only hide the tin-opener. Instant satisfaction is all. (But not in all things. As I say, we do sex later in the book.)

Others lose their appetites. And some just develop strange ones: coal, banana pizza, cream soda, that kind of thing. They say it's your body craving something it lacks. But it could just be natural vileness you normally repress being released by your rampaging hormones. Husbands who married anti-veal, pro-textured vegetable protein women have been known to discover them by the fridge door, jaws practically dripping blood as they shove in whole slices of pig, pausing only to dip them in the mustard pot.

Sometimes you go off things. The damnable thing is that it's rarely Hob-Nobs, Mars bars or crumpets dripping with butter you go off. I went off seafood, which is practically calorie-free. Love the stuff. In a hotel in Cornwall, eight weeks pregnant with the first one, I ordered the ocean bed on a plate, not knowing my foetus loathed lobster and the like. When it arrived, I could only nibble the hard-boiled egg and the lettuce. We made our excuses and went to our room in quick time, unable to understand the smirk on our waitress's face. Then we saw our room key fob had 'honeymoon suite' all over it. It was the only room they had. . . .

B *is for...*

Beanbag

Great for having babies on. Even more supportive in the labour room than an aromatherapist-acupuncturist playing cassettes of dolphins making love. Choose any position from frog thrown tummy-first against rock to squatting garden gnome notices his open fly.

No one ever looks great giving birth on a beanbag. You'll need a loving partner and a midwife with young knees.

By the way, we're not talking those silly little bean-bags you chucked around in junior PE, or the middle-sized ones you bought before you could afford proper furniture. We're talking absolutely enormous, take-the-weight-of-a-fourteen-stone-desperate-woman beanbags which don't split when you gnaw them.

Labour wards are full of little midwives with ridiculously small waists. The beanbag is probably the only thing you will see in the whole place which is bigger than you are. Fling yourself upon it. If that's physically impossible, demand a crane.

Being there

You have no choice. Has he? A generation or two ago the husbands were out in the corridor or on the golf course, or downstairs at home boiling kettles. Nobody ever asked what all that hot water was for. Tea and to keep the husband occupied was probably the honest answer. First of all, Being There became fashionable and then it became compulsory. New Men find it a mystical experience and recount it endlessly to their friends, awestruck by their partner's performance. The partner, who knows it was hell through gritted teeth, begins to wonder if she was actually at the same event. Men can be very boring about it. Especially those who refer to it as 'Just amazing. The greatest moment of my life.' That's the trouble with New Man – he reads all the pregnancy books, he buys the empathy belly, he helps you write your birth plan. But, sister, he knows nothing. Nothing.

And you have to find something for him to do. Men are not used to spectator sports where there are no mates, no beers and no end in sight to extra time. Mopping your brow with scented tissues takes only so long and is a bit tame as his half of a Shared Life Experience. Some hospitals let the fathers cut the umbilical cord to make them feel important. Fine, but it still doesn't kill much time in the average labour. Decide beforehand whether you want him around your head or your baby's head. Once they've seen the gore and the mire, some men apparently can't Do It for ages. But then again some women are rather relieved.

My heart warms to the chaps who rub your back and squeeze your hand at the time, and afterwards admit it was hell. For them. There is now a swing among men towards Being Anywhere But There.

Birth partners

Normally the child's father, but sometimes a friend or relation, who stays with you for the birth. It's got to be someone close, who will love you whatever you say in the throes of labour. Avoid anyone who is normally the life and soul of the party. This is no party. And mad snappers should be avoided too. Think: do you really want polaroids of your haemorrhoids?

Birth plan

This is the bit of paper you spend ages writing weeks before the birth and remember ruefully afterwards. It's worth doing, though. You state the sort of labour you would like and it stops the medical profession treating you like a brainless barrage balloon booked in for deflation. Patient choice? Get real. This is birth, not an *à la carte* dinner.

State your preference for pain relief, the position in which you want to give birth, whether you mind students having a look-in and whether you want a physiological third stage or syntometrine. In other words, a jab to make the placenta come away or a natural delivery.

Birth plans should not be used by birth partners to beat you around the head. 'Come on, now. It's really not that bad. You say here "no pain relief no matter what I say at the time". Stop chewing the carpet and concentrate on your breathing exercises.'

Good birth plans include lots of get-out clauses such as 'I may not be as brave as I think I am' and 'I am definitely not as brave as my partner thinks I am', and 'I would be a good guinea pig for any untried method of utterly painless childbirth'.

My birth plan was a joke. After being wired to every-thing except the national grid during my first labour, I didn't write one the next time. But the original was there in my notes when I checked in for baby number two. Hospitals often keep them. 'I'd like as natural a birth as possible,' I'd written. Innocent, hopeful fool. You may, like me, the second time around get the birth you wanted first time around.

Birth report

The birth plan is how you'd like it. The birth report is how it really was. NCT teachers love them. It's their way of researching their subject without having to go through the gruelling business too often themselves. Of course, you'll get a report of sorts from the hospital – probably a computer print-out with your baby's weight, your method of pain relief and your length of labour. (The last one is always a lie. See *Labour*.) But it won't mention the fact that you scoffed three pot noo-dles between three and five centimetres' dilation; that you attempted to vasectomize your husband with a pair of surgical tweezers; that your language lost some of its maiden purity, or that you called for bigger and better pain relief while eating your aromatherapy relax-you candles. NCT or not, it's worth writing down your own memory of labour when you have the time, if only to record some of the eccentricities, especially of the early first stage. There are women who iron like crazy, even socks. There are women who distractedly try to cook things in the fridge, or suddenly find something incredibly banal – like sewing nametapes on an older child's sports gear – becomes absolutely urgent. I know of one woman who washed out an empty tin of cat food and left it neatly on the draining board before ringing her husband's office with the message: 'Please could you tell him his wife is having a baby now?' There was a Fleet Street rumour some years ago of a woman who had left an answerphone message saying that she was now in the hospital and she would see him in the labour ward. Unfortunately, she'd left it on her previous husband's answerphone.

Bladder

You may not actually be waving yours in the air on a stick, but suddenly a Morris man's obsession with his will seem mild compared to yours. You'll be constantly peeing into bottles for antenatal checks. Much easier to use a jug and then decant, by the way. NHS receptacles are made with men in mind.

Your bladder will wake you up at the beginning and end of your pregnancy. It will leak. It's all due to the pressure of the womb on everything beneath. It lifts mid-pregnancy when your baby lifts out of the pelvis. After the birth you pee like mad as your body loses all the excess fluid.

Blood

Well, the periods stop. But remember, when you have that baby, you don't need neat little tampons or slim, allegedly absorbent pads. You need utterly enormous, thick, soft maternity towels. Lots of them – two at a time per night – for the first few days. The postnatal blood is called 'lochia' and it keeps coming, sometimes beyond your six-week postnatal check.

Doctors and visiting midwives after the birth will want to know all about what they call your 'loss'. They will want to know if it's red, brown or yellow. They even want to know if it has lumps in it, for heaven's sake.

They're not hairdressers asking where you went on holiday, so do not be tempted to make things up just to add interest to their job. They will ask you to produce any oddities for their inspection.

B/O

This hieroglyph on your daily medical notes does not refer to your armpits. It means 'bowels open'. Another of those little shared intimacies between you and your midwife. It may seem like nosiness but, believe me, if you've had stitches, you can put off a B/O scenario for an unbelievable length of time.

Blooming

Somewhere between the tired-as-death first three months and the please-let-it-be-over-soon last three months, some women bloom. They look like the women in the Other Pregnancy Books. Their hair

shines, they have pink cheeks and lots of energy. The
rest of us hate them. We're all supposed to be like that.
Just as brides are radiant, mothers-to-be are blooming.
In fact, I felt more like the mother of the bride –
dressed as a ship in full sail, inclined to be emotional
and trying to keep off the bottle.

Blues

Baby blues come in with the milk, about three or four
days after the birth. Rioting hormones can make the
sanest of us go crackers for a while. I actually thought
a train was going through my bedroom one night. It
passes in a few days – the blues, not the train. Hold
tight to baby, husband and sleep. Pay someone to clean
the house and do the ironing. Put the answerphone on
and avoid *Old bats* (see later).

Body

Well, you've done it no favours. A waistline which has
expanded into the second tape-measure is not going to
snap back like a piece of elastic. Unless you're about
sixteen. You can either shrug your shoulders and say
farewell to all that or work out. There are men who
prefer the softer, more substantial version of woman-
hood. If he buys you an exercise book, as mine did,
yours isn't one of them.

Bowels

There's no getting away from it: they sometimes empty
during the birth. There's a baby coming down head-first
(if you're lucky) and anything in the way gets shifted.

It's as simple as that. The midwife has seen it all before. And your husband should be cooling your brow, not examining your plumbing. You can attempt to manage things by eating lots of fruit and vegetable before your due date in the hope that things will take their course sooner rather than later. Do beware that feeling of needing desperately to go to the loo during labour. Signals get very confused around the undercarriage and that pressing need could just be the baby coming down.

Bras

'Triumph has the bra for the way you are', the ad says. But, if you're pregnant, listen instead to comedian Jo Brand: 'Does it hell. Isambard Kingdom Brunel has the bra for the way I am.'

Pregnancy does things to your breasts: they weigh a pound or two heavier, thanks to all those milk-producing cells, and in your first pregnancy at least you will probably be bursting out of your bra. You can't get much which is uncantilevered, let alone pretty, in a 38E. I found a mulberry-coloured job in a sale tub and rejoiced. Actually, twin tubs would have been even better than the bra. Just £6.50 it was.

Trouble is, you forget what you're wearing underneath. I wriggled out of my top for the doctor to take my blood pressure at an antenatal check and there it was – the colour of those two-part Swiss cherry yoghurts after you've stirred the fruit in. I said nothing. The doctor said nothing. But I could see she suspected I had the matching knickers.

The biggest brassiere problem I've heard of was a tiny but voluptuous friend who shot up from a 32DD to a 36HH by nursing-bra time. Networking through the entire country, she found one bra.

Braxton Hicks

If I ever write a thriller, I shall have a conman, an imposter, a plausible chap called Braxton Hicks. He will be nothing like his real beastly self. Braxton Hicks contractions are what they call the hardening of the womb in the last few weeks of pregnancy. Practice contractions, they are. Suddenly your stomach goes rock hard, but don't panic. You probably have a long, long time to go yet. They are nothing like the real thing. The real thing you cannot miss.

Breastfeeding

Everyone should do it. Buy the nursing bra, the sleep bra, the breast pads, the old-fashioned camomile-based nipple cream while you're pregnant. And afterwards watch the milk head for the ceiling with each orgasm.

Breastfeeding adds a whole new meaning to the phrase 'wet T-shirt'. There's a lot of soaking up to do when having a baby. Breast pads are soft paper things which stop wet marks on your jumper. Lactating breasts tend to operate in pairs. The one you're not using at the time spurts at the beginning of the feed too. (See *Milk* and *Old farts*)

Breasts

They get big and warm – very suddenly with your first pregnancy. The men in the office begin to stare. Husbands and partners who have always said: 'You're just right as you are. I like small breasts,' start drooling and show a desire to lose themselves in your jumper. For years they've just been polite. Like us, they know size counts really.

Breathing

This is the sacred cow of many an antenatal class. You can spend several evenings learning how to breathe. It's enough to make you wonder how you've got by in ignorance for so long. Committed breathers say it helps you relax in labour and manage your contractions. But many women find they just do what comes naturally or what the midwife tells them to do at the time. Counting your outbreaths while operating a TENS machine or gas-and-air mask is like patting your head and rubbing your tummy at the same time – practically impossible and of limited use.

Bumps

They vary in size, shape and height. Everyone will have an opinion on whether you're expecting a boy (all at the front) or a girl (all over). All a lot of rot? Why worry when the bump may actually be hairy too? It's caused by an increase in male hormones during pregnancy. Unless it's the full moon, of course. In which case check the palms of your hands.

C *is for . . .*

Caesarean

The designer version of childbirth if it's by choice. Like designer clothes, if you have a tiny pelvis, this is for you. You get an epidural, a good seat and you stay awake. If it's what they call non-elective (ie a rush job because it's the best way to get the baby out fast), you'll have a general anaesthetic. Either way, the surgeon cuts the abdomen and uterus and lifts the baby out. These days they go for a bikini cut. You'll be sore afterwards, but at least you don't get harassed by midwives asking if you've started exercising yet.

Camomile tea

Very continental. So calming when you're pregnant.

But a dead give-away at the office if you're normally a caffeine and gin freak.

Castor oil

Sorry to keep on about bowels. There are women who get so fed up after forty weeks that they swallow a cocktail of orange juice and castor oil to get things moving. I'd rather go overdue on white wine and more white wine myself, but it's a tried and tested method. Empty bowels give the baby room to drop and increase the pressure on the cervix.

Cats

Smug creatures, cats. Boy, are they about to get their comeuppance. Don't expect them to like the creature who has usurped their place on your lap. If you insist on keeping your moggy (you've guessed it – I don't like 'em much), it's worth hunting around before the birth for an old-fashioned cat net. Puss asleep on baby must be every cat-owning mother's nightmare. Don't be fobbed off with an insect net – it's much too gauzy. You need the sort with big holes which cats really hate catching their paws in. And don't change cat litter while you're pregnant: there's a risk of toxoplasmosis which can cause foetal brain damage.

Clothes

Soon clothes for work become a problem. I'd never gone in for the executive tart look – all those little red jackets and even smaller black stretch skirts, but I'd never touched an elasticated waistband either. As far as I was concerned, they were a short step away from American Tan tights and to be avoided at all costs. But when I looked round for maternity clothes, I was amazed by how few there were. Oh, there were lots of navy blue dresses with white collars – there seemed to be a conspiracy among the fashion industry to make all pregnant women look like old-fashioned waitresses who had sneaked too many cream horns. But nothing you'd actually like to wear. 'Who does good maternity clothes?' I asked our very thin and childless fashion department at the *Daily Express*, where I then worked. 'Just buy your favourite designer in a big size,' came back the reply. Ahem. I have no designer, favourite or otherwise.

'Oh, my God, it won't meet.' I was face to waist with the ghastly truth in the office loo when changing into a black chiffon culottes outfit for an evening dinner job. Two colleagues kept my culottes up with an arrangement of safety-pins and elastic bands which I committed to memory for later use. All was well until my next visit to the loo – just after the paté. I had to miss the main course to cope with the contraption.

Thereafter it was baggy harem-style trousers and big jumpers, and flat pixie boots; I jumped into them all far too soon, of course. Later I realized the *raison d'être* of the maternity dress, though not of its white collar. Things with waists slide below the bump, bringing the crotch of harem pants down to knee level.

Pregnant women tend to fall into one of three clothes categories: the Earth Mother in flowing Monsoon dresses handprinted by genuine Amazonian vegetable-dyed Indians, the Cream Horn Waitress, or Dungaree Dyke.

The thing to do is to trawl the small ads in women's magazines for companies which specialize in dressing the bump for business meetings, leisure, the lot. Some of them do matching children's clothes as well. Send off for the catalogue. Make sure you don't ring the number for the exotic lingerie and crotchless knickers in the next column.

Colostrum

Thick yellowy stuff secreted by your breasts in the days before the milk comes in. For some time before the birth you may see evidence of it on your nipples. It's full of antibodies which protect the baby from infection. When my first baby brought some colostrum up on her sleepsuit I rang for the duty midwife, convinced in the gloom of the labour ward that she was coughing up blood. And that was before the nuttiness of baby blues. Not to be confused with colostomy, an altogether different bag.

Conception

The fun bit nine months before the tough bit. If it doesn't happen, there may be a reason as simple as tight Y-fronts. Healthy sperm need to hang loose and chill out. Rip the Y-fronts off with your teeth, buy him some breezy boxers and go through the whole hellish performance again. And again. Failing that, get help.

Contraception

At the end of a pregnancy you can't believe you'll ever need contraception again, certainly not before the six-week postnatal check. In spite of having squeezed this melon out, the idea of putting even something six inches by three-ish (okay, I've never measured it) in the same space seems incredible. This leads to a lot of babies just ten months older than their big brother or sister. Even if you normally deal with contraception, send him to the chemist. It's that condom moment.

Contractions

They're the tightenings of the womb which open up the cervix and push the baby out. What does a contraction feel like? Put it this way: the gaps in between are bliss. Contractions can be so intense that you feel sleepy in between them.

They start short and spaced out. Then they lengthen, intensify and eventually start coming every couple of minutes. Each one has a build-up, a peak, and a fading away. And, yes, they hurt.

How do you cope? You've no option. It's a one-way ticket. Some like to blow hard with every outbreath and rock to and fro; others lie down and yell for every method of pain relief going, while swearing at their partners and shredding their natural childbirth 'I believe in endorphins' birth plan. And then there are those who contract on the move. They go for a walk, pausing to squat for a contraction, or they stride up and down the stairs. Every which way, there's no going back. (See *Endorphins*)

Cramp

Real omigod cramp in the middle of the night, usually in the calves, because your muscles are working harder carrying an extra, unbalanced load about. Flat heels during the day stop your calf muscles from being bunched up. When it happens, force your heel right down to stretch the muscle. Increasing your salt intake will help. A great excuse for eating crisps in bed.

Curry

'Go for a hot curry,' you'll probably be told when your baby is overdue. What it does is get the bowel moving, make a bit more space and ginger things up round there. Indian waiters assume (or you think they do) a knowing look when heavily pregnant women squeeze themselves on to their red velour banquettes and ask for 'something a bit hotter than usual'. Remember, if you're a Biryani type, that waiter has rumbled you and knows that you won't be coming in again for years once the baby is born. He will probably go right into that kitchen and reach for the vindaloo powder, and you'll have streaming eyes all the way home and wish you'd had the orange juice and castor oil your mother recommended instead.

Cystitis

More common in pregnancy, just when you're likely to be going to the loo a lot anyway. If you're a natural-is-best freak, try drinking lots of cranberry juice to prevent as well as cure.

D *is for...*

Decorating

Women do a lot of this when pregnant. It's a form of
Nesting (see later). Women whose idea of decorating is
leaving the tidemark in the bath suddenly start wondering whether the baby would prefer Tuscan Terra-
cotta or Cloud Blue on the sitting-room walls. No baby
is actually going to notice the paintwork, but then no
baby ever learnt its alphabet from all those ABC blan-
kets and cot bumpers. It doesn't stop you doing it and
buying them.

One woman I know was poised on the bathside,
eight months pregnant and painting the bathroom
walls, when her husband came in and asked her just
what she thought she was doing. He installed her on
the sofa with a cup of tea and a book. An hour later he

heard her cry out. She was back in the bathroom again, stuck between the wall and the loo, desperately trying to paint behind the cistern. The day before her baby was due she embarked on a patchwork cot quilt.

Career women go into domestic overdrive when pregnant. All those years of powering ahead are put to one side for the sake of homemaking. Nothing stops them until the baby arrives and stops everything. There are reports of really overdue women lining their briefcases with Laura Ashley fabric left-overs, having run out of domestic surfaces to cover.

Dilation

You thought this what just what your pupils did when expressing sexual attraction? Well it's also what your cervix (neck of the womb) does with the help of contractions nine and a half months later. It's followed by an amazing opening-up feeling, if you're not too heavily doped, as the baby passes through.

But dilation is an elusive thing. Some women start dilating and then stop for a while, especially with a first birth. I was actually advised to go back home from hospital when my cervix lost interest in the whole thing. I refused and buried my head in *Teach Yourself Italian*, pausing for the occasional contraction. By the time I reached full dilation (ten centimetres) I could have translated Dante.

A traffic jam, even just the move from home to the hospital, can throw the body off course and slow the contractions right down. Hospitals get the adrenaline going in all of us and adrenaline is the natural enemy of the relaxation your body wants.

You're convinced the Mersey Tunnel must have opened up in there by now, but the midwife pulls her fingers out and shakes her head. 'Still three centimetres?' you wail. 'How much longer?' To which the only honest reply is: 'Another seven centimetres.'

Doctors

Totally unnecessary in routine pregnancies and births. But they tend to get in on the act somehow. In some health authorities antenatal care is given mainly by doctors, either at hospital clinics or in GP practices. And in labour wards they're difficult to escape. Useful when things go wrong, of course. The trouble is, however things are going, doctors usually want to act.

I was beached in the labour room with my first baby – contractions sluggish, dilation suspended, *Teach Yourself Italian* steaming ahead – and in swept the doctor, students in tow. He ruptured my membranes (broke the waters with that massive crochet hook) and for good measure stuck a monitoring clip on my unborn baby's scalp. Then he swept out, leaving me on a layer or two of soggy tissues with a length of coiled wire sticking up between my legs.

Sure he asked my permission, but by then I'd have said yes to anything, even a tin-opener. By law all you need is a midwife at the birth.

Doing it yourself

Well, doing It yourself won't get you pregnant, but what I'm talking about here is DIY birth. There are people out there (mainly afterbirth eaters, for which see *Placenta*) who've watched their cat produce her litter with no birth partner, no anaesthetist and no trouble. And they think they're the same.

'Why not be like that cat?' they think. Ask the cat what she thought of it first, I reckon.

But, if you want to curl up in a basket with a blanket and get on with it alone, what's to stop you? The law, actually. You can be prosecuted for intentionally giving birth without a midwife or a doctor. Most radical birth people reckon that you'd only get into trouble with the law if you did the whole bit, including cutting the cord, without calling for help.

If DIY birth happens to you, intentionally or other-wise, catch that baby and keep it warm.

Domino

Many of us in that category between the earth mother and those who need an aspirin for a cough like the idea of a domino birth. Getting one is a different matter. Domino isn't about getting spotty and falling over: it stands for domiciliary in and out. You book a domino with your community midwife and usually she'll be in charge of most of your antenatal care. When you go into labour, you ring your community midwife. She comes to see you at home, or at least rings you up a lot. Then you jointly decide when to go to hospital and the same midwife delivers your baby there. About six hours later, you go home and the midwife comes to see you there. It's a great cross between home and hospital birth, and you build up a good relationship with your midwife, which some research suggests leads to less intervention in labour. But it's not available in all areas, and even where it is available, numbers are lim-ited. Your midwife may not be free when you go into

labour. You may want to go to hospital early. You may
find leaving hospital within six hours is wildly opti-
mistic, especially if the baby arrives late in the day.
Timing can be tricky: because you're at home with
your midwife, you feel less inclined to leave early for
the hospital and you can find yourself desperate to
push when you're in the lift going up to the labour
ward. Many more dominos are booked than actually
happen. Having said that, it's worth a go. There's a lot
to be said for sleeping in your own bed with your new
baby. And for months afterwards, you can regale your
wide-eyed friends with your story of how you went in
after breakfast and were home for supper or before
your older children came back from school.

Dropped

As in 'the baby's dropped'. Somewhat alarming, but all
it means is that the baby's head has engaged in the
pelvis and your whole bump has lowered. It makes
breathing easier, which is good news. But it increases
the pressure on the bladder, which can be a dampener.

Due date

This is the medical profession's idea of a joke on a
pregnant woman. They get very keen on the idea of a
date: they scan you and measure bits of your foetus.
During my first pregnancy my baby's head was several
days older than her femur, yet she was born in one
piece. They measure the bump, which oh so conve-
niently grows at the rate of a centimetre per week. And
they quiz you on the length of your menstrual cycle. All
this to establish a due date. Around five per cent of

babies arrive on the due date, so what's the point? I had one baby twenty-one days late, one induced at twenty-two days late and one just four days late. So much for that.

Dull ache

In your lower back? Could be the real due date.

E *is for...*

Earth mothers

Earth mothers are a definite type, but rarely think of themselves that way. They have several children and stay at home to look after them for years. They breast-feed them forever and then cook them real food. When pregnant, they wear the floaty cotton variety of maternity clothes and get very big. They eschew all forms of testing except scans. The ultimate earth mother has a water birth, at home, with no pain relief. And then makes breakfast for everyone in the morning.

Earth mothers don't mind about stretch-marks or floppy tummies. The trouble with being an earth mother is that other people, not just your children, sense comfort and want to cuddle up to your bosom or hang on your apron strings. Because earth mothers are very positive about their motherhood, their children and the way they live their lives, even childfree-by-choice career bitches don't dismiss them lightly. The earth mother herself may have doubts, but she seems so capable and together that no one can see them.

What happens to the earth mother when the earthlings have all gone to school? Why she slips another one in before the menopause. Then she starts a little catering or knitwear design business from home, while becoming either a school governor, magistrate or adult literacy teacher.

Eating for two

Oh, yeah? You have the only foetus who needs extra chips?

Elasticated waistbands

Don't laugh. You'll need them. Probably for the rest of your life. No? Do you have any idea how many sit-ups it takes? And how little time you'll have to do them?

Elderly primigravida

Not an overweight and ancient ballerina, but an insulting term for anyone daring to have her first baby over whatever age the medical profession reckons is best at the moment. Now that the average age for having a first baby is twenty-eight, the term seems to be dropping out of use. (See also *Age*)

Embryo

That's an embryo you have inside you for the first eight weeks. By then it has fingers and toes, for heaven's sake. Buy one of those books with in-womb pictures and be amazed. But don't expect full colour on your scan pictures later on. After the first eight weeks it's called a foetus, and all it's doing is growing. Mothers, being contemptibly unscientific and sentimental creatures, tend to think of it as a baby all the time.

Empathy bellies

Pillow-type garments men can strap on to see how it feels to be pregnant. Truly. What's odd is that no one has marketed a method of making men feel sick, tired out, unattractive and fed up with swollen ankles.

Endorphins

Who needs drugs when we have endorphins, the body's natural pain relief? They're relaxing hormones secreted by the brain. No needles, no gas masks. Sounds good? So why do we get headaches?

Epidural

Unnatural, very effective pain relief via a very big needle put in your back. Some women swear by it. I had it first time round after a long time trying to do without it. It takes a little while to set up, so don't leave it until you're roaring. When I saw the anaesthetist I could have kissed him.

Epidural anaesthetists tend to have a somewhat jaundiced attitude towards drug-free birth plans. A friend of mine swears the man who put her out of all pain walked into the labour room with a half-eaten sandwich sticking out of his pocket, looked at her and said, 'So the lavender oil and hypnosis let you down?'

Episiotomy

A cut to help the baby out. Some hospitals do it more often than others. The fact is that the baby's coming out one way or another. Some women prefer to tear. Some midwives believe a cut limits the damage. But tears heal better. The smaller the baby the less likelihood of either. If you tear once, you're likely to tear again, but it's not inevitable. I tore first and second times but not third. Old-style midwives pride themselves on avoiding cuts and tears. Quite right too. Did Coco Chanel's buttons burst the buttonholes?

Exercise

They do two incredible things to you after you've had your baby in hospital. They come round to discuss birth control, as if you could ever need it again. And they give you exercise sheets. Don't worry. There is one you'll be able to do. I don't mean the first-day ankle-rotation and pelvic floor exercises. I mean the one at the end of the sheet that says: 'Put a pillow under your tummy and rest.'

After your first baby, you'll probably go more or less back into shape. Try not to be too smug. The second one will do for you. Thereafter you'll actually look your fittest when six or so months pregnant, because it takes up the slack.

After my second baby, I took to an exercise machine. I would lie there, legs up in the air, the memories flooding back. Mainly memories of stirrups and stitches, actually.

Occasionally I still waddle on to the old flab contraption and go like mad at it for a week or two. As an incentive I hang an old skirt with an impossibly small waist outside the bedroom where I see it as I exercise.

I never thought I'd see the day. A long and noble career as an anti-exercise campaigner has met a formidable opponent, seven extra inches which have made my waist disappear. Three babies, combined birth weight 28lbs 9oz, have forced my hand – into my wallet for the best torture contraption Argos had to offer.

As I do leg presses, lat pull-downs (arm exercises) and sit-ups (my husband has given up watching television) I reflect that I am not the woman I once was. What has happened to the girl who stood resolutely on the sideline, freezing in culottes, as others ran round keeping warm with hockey sticks raised; who stood in the queue for the vaulting horse, but somehow never made it to the front; who was usually found by a fuming games mistress in the last alcove of the library during netball practice?

I have resisted them all in my time. Just watching others on sports day made me tired. Years later friends spent their evenings toning and groaning. Not I. Why go for the burn when you could go for a tandoori? And, more recently, why go to step aerobics when you live in a house with six flights? I have avoided mirror-clad gyms and their lycra-clad skinnies for years. I'd never be caught out with legs akimbo like the Princess of Wales, that was for sure. Pineapple was for eating, not for emblazoning across a leotard and a sweating chest. Now, of course, any paparazzo could sneak in and find me resplendent in baggy trousers and sweater, with my legs even higher than ordered by the midwife when she was doing the stitches.

The contraption is not a thing of beauty itself and puts you through a lot of short-term ugliness. Home gyms make you sweat and go red all over. They should come with curtains, like a shower. And, reader, if ever you find yourself resorting to leg presses, make sure the man is out of the room. Maybe the cat as well.

My idea of exercise has always been gentle swimming. Breaststroke, of course, chin above water, and preferably going up and down the pool with a good friend to chat to. You emerge from the pool feeling great but with an appetite like Dawn French. Even an appetite for Dawn French. Women-only sessions at our local pool are usually followed by get-fat-with-froth cappuccino sessions in the café.

Some friends and relations (not, I bitterly note, my husband) have suggested the home gym is rather extreme. They have not been there. They have not tried on skirt after skirt and ended up back in maternity dresses. They have not had to suffer the indignity of being asked, six months postnatal, 'When is the baby due, dear?' They have not counted, as I have, fifteen skirts, two pairs of trousers and one pair of jeans which will not do up – the items now hanging outside the bedroom door to encourage me. 'Buy new,' they say. Oh, fine. Find me some jeans which will fit my unchanged hips and my new-look waist and I'll buy them in six colours.

'Diet,' they say. Look, this resists diets. Losing weight is easy, if you want to. You just stop putting so much fattening food in your mouth. Putting the ping back into muscles which have stretched well into a second tape-measure is bloody hard work. But I want my waist back. I am tired of living in dresses. They make me feel about twelve.

I have looked at this stomach in the mirror every morning since my third baby. It is a long, narrow mirror and the stomach fills it disconcertingly. My husband bought me, a day or two before Valentine's Day, a 6op book called *How To Regain Your Figure After Pregnancy*. The pressure.

'It could be worse,' said a friend who'd had four children and was still floating round in loose Indian dresses when the youngest went to nursery school. 'I had underwear. He gave me lovely stuff, all in my pre-pregnancy size.' She's still wearing the oddly coloured bargain bras in huge sizes that she bought to see herself through the brimming cups of pregnancy. She's hoping her husband will forget the size she used to be and the underwear he bought her, but the lime-green and maroon DDs keep giving her away.

'You'll need music,' said the exercise experts. Quite right. 'For the rhythm,' they said. Quite wrong. For noise. The cartilage or whatever it is in the knees actually creaks and crackles when I do my leg extensions.

I need a contraption, something to tackle. I need a receipt of purchase in my wallet. I find value for money an incentive. The prospect of a pat on the head from my doctor at the six-week postnatal check was not. No chance of it anyway.

'Everyone does the safe sit-up these days,' said a colleague, who has her own step, for heaven's sake. And I don't mean outside her front door. Safe? There'd never been any danger of a sit-up at all as far as I was concerned. But now – sometimes for a fortnight at a time – I'm at it every evening, sitting-up, bench-pressing, the lot.

Sometimes I think I discern the beginning of an inward curve where my waist used to be. Or am I looking in a wider mirror?

F *is for...*

F-words

There's a rule in labour which says that the purer your speech normally, the fouler it will be while giving birth. All that repressed naughtiness is unlocked by pain, pethidine or gas and air, and the obscenities fly. Total fishwives, on the other hand, tend to restrict themselves to an occasional heartfelt oath. Neither puritan nor fishwife, I muttered the occasional 'Oh dear, oh dear'.

Farting and burping

Hardly what you expect from a woman in bloom, but there's a lot of pressure upwards and downwards as the womb expands. Escapes are inevitable. So what excuse do men have for doing it all the time?

Father of the baby

We have to include him otherwise he'd feel left out. On and off he's going to feel left out for years, whereas as you will often feel you've been let in for more than you could possibly have imagined.

Worthy pregnancy mags and books often include the routine 'I'm having a baby too' piece written by a man. This is absolute nonsense, as a quick look in any labour ward will tell you. All the empathy bellies on all the New Men in the world will not alter the fact that babies don't grow in men.

But if you want him to stay around, you have to include him. Let him stroke your tummy and talk to the baby, as the Other Pregnancy Books suggest. It won't do any harm and it will keep the poor sod happy.

Feelings

Pregnant women can be emotional. Blame the hormones. Demand absolute indulgence. Weep profusely, but apologetically, if you don't get it at first. You can get away with all sorts of things – not going to parties with people you hate; not letting him go out with the boys; not having his mother round – when you're pregnant. A good line is: 'Let's enjoy our time as just a couple while we can.' This is at-home advice only. If you indulge the hormones at work, they'll just put you down as unstable.

Feet

They swell. So do your ankles and fingers. Especially towards the end of the pregnancy. By then there's an extra twelve pints of fluid swishing about your body, and only half of that's in the womb. The rest is obeying gravity and heading for your feet.

Beware of taking your shoes off unless you're going to put your feet up: you probably won't be able to get them back on. Your shoes will stretch and be too big for you after the birth. The fluid may even get worse in the day or two after the birth. Then you start peeing like mad.

Another foot problem is that the bump makes reaching your toenails pretty hard. Your man will have to cut them for you. Buy some nice foot oils and powders: he might as well do a pedicure while he's down there. Anything else is a private matter between the two of you.

Flat on your back

The old-fashioned way of giving birth. How this persisted for so many generations after Isaac Newton discovered gravity is a mystery. On second thoughts, it's not. It persisted because it gives the medical profession the best view of your undercarriage and the baby. But midwives and doctors have knees and are rather more agile than a labouring woman. Let them bend. The baby wants to come out, not put on a slow-moving cabaret show.

Of course, if you have an epidural, you're likely to end up at least semi-recumbent. But squatting, kneeling, leaning are all better. They open up your pelvis and it's much easier to push. A recent UK survey showed that over half of women still deliver lying down. The shorter the labour the more likely you are to manage it without lying down. But then, if you don't lie down, you're more likely to have a shorter labour. Ask Isaac.

Flying

Airlines generally won't fly you after twenty-eight weeks of pregnancy for insurance reasons. And, frankly, you probably won't want to anyway. Flying plays hell with gravity and fluid, and you'll roll off the plane with ankles the size of an air hostess's waist.

Food in labour

A friend ate hospital fish and chips during labour, and found they gave her strength. The midwives made me eat and I found it made me sick. Up to you. The conventional advice is carbohydrate – pasta, perhaps – while the contractions are still few and far between. It gives you energy later when you need it and takes a long time to burn up. And, after all, getting hold of salt, vinegar and mushy peas in the labour ward won't be easy.

Friends

During the last few weeks you'll be bored stupid and want to talk to them all the the time. As you go overdue, they'll want to talk to you all the time, while you get fed up with 'Haven't you had that baby yet?' conversations. Afterwards, put the answerphone on.

Babies are unbelievably you-consuming. You need to be able to call on your friends rather than have them call on you. And you'll be amazed by how little interest you have in office gossip.

Fun

If your baby is overdue and you have an older midwife, at some stage she will nudge you or your husband and say: 'What you should do is go home and have a bit of Fun.' What she means to say is that the prostaglandins in your husband's semen will help the cervix to ripen. The trouble is that by this stage in the pregnancy you will have foresworn sex for life and your husband would need to be as flexible as an Anglepoise lamp to do the necessary with the old prostaglandins. And any intelligent sperm would probably be thinking: 'What's the point of all this? Talk about coals to Newcastle. I'm not going all that way.' My husband told his mother what the midwife had said. 'Fun?' she replied. 'Ooh, no. I don't think Jill's in a fit state to go to Thorpe Park.' (See *Nipples*)

G *is for...*

Gas and air

Wouldn't have a baby without it, I thought after my second baby. Then the third one arrived before the midwife could give me the all-important mouthpiece. I never had a whiff.

Some weeks before a home birth the community midwife comes with the cannister, but the mouthpiece comes at the birth and no sooner. They say it's because they're very expensive pieces of equipment and they don't want them knocking around your broom cupboard for weeks. But the real reason is that you might call in all your friends, get gassed up and have a hell of a party. And that was how I found out that gas and air isn't vital, though probably more fun.

Posh name is Entonox. It's half oxygen and half nitrous oxide (laughing gas) and you breathe it in. 'Made me swear like a trooper,' some women say. It gives you a lift and helps you cope with the pain towards the end of the first stage. In the second stage of my second birth I hung onto the mouthpiece like a comforter. And it gave me something to bite when I got tired of the beanbag.

Gas and air comes in big cannisters. Some women get through two, they're having such a good time. Not to be confused with Calor Gas, though it could make for a very high camping holiday.

Gender

At the end of the day that's a baby you've got, not a gender. It's a little person who will soon wipe out whatever preferences you might have had before the birth. And, anyway, they all look like an elder statesman, even the ones in pink. I always thought I'd never be able to handle a boy – all that rumbustious behaviour, that business of learning to pee standing up and with some sort of accuracy, that physical need to wrestle the furniture into submission. And the fact that my son has proved me absolutely right makes me love him not one jot the less.

By the way, the nurture not nature argument is laughably up the creek. Girls and boys are made differently. There are tomboy girls and there are gentle boys, but by and large treating them scrupulously alike is a waste of time and energy.

G is for . . .

Gums

There's an old saying: 'A tooth for every baby.' Weird idea. Perhaps fluoride toothpaste and regular flossing have sorted that one out. But gums do sometimes bleed in pregnancy. It's called gingivitis and is caused by the extra blood in your body. Luckily you get free dental treatment while pregnant and for a year afterwards. Worth trying to swing that costly bridgework now?

Grapefruit

Nothing to do with diet and everything to do with what you feel as if you have between your legs in the last weeks of your first pregnancy. The baby's head is engaged in your pelvis and – unlike in later pregnancies, when it moves around in the extra space – it's staying there. Which gives you the grapefruit gait. You'll never laugh at ducks out of water again. And the oddest thing of all is when your grapefruit starts to hiccup.

Grunting

Some women in labour make Monica Seles sound like a mewing kitten. Bearing down makes them grunt with sheer effort. But then others fart. It's bad luck if you do both, but it could be worse still. And probably will be. (See *Bowels*)

H *is for...*

Hair

The 'blooming' theory is that it thickens during pregnancy and shines – all clever hormonal stuff to keep the male with the female and so safeguard the infant. But for how long? Round about three months after the birth it drops out alarmingly in cushion-stuffing quantities. Things return to normal after that, but why is it so grey?

Heartburn

Of course, you could have an ulcer. But that pain high in your chest or in your back is most likely to be heartburn. There's nothing equal to pregnancy for making you feel like a Rennies-chewing granny. You even have ankles and fingers the same as hers. What's happening is that the hormones, on alert to make things slack for the birth, slacken the valve at the top of the stomach too and acid problems follow. Hit the milk of magnesia. Take comfort – it's worse if you're expecting twins. Or maybe you are.

Heart rate

Throughout your pregnancy the doctor or midwife will listen to the baby's heart rate. It's twice as fast as an adult heart – between 120 and 160 beats per minute. An old wives' tale passed on to me by my GP says that boys have low heart rates and girls have high. Certainly true in the case of my children.

Hiccups

Not yours, the baby's. Upside down (with any luck) and swallowing amniotic fluid greedily, the baby may well get hiccups. And you will feel them, strange regular little jumps low down in your womb. The muscles needed for regular breathing aren't fully developed yet.

Home versus hospital

In the space of three generations home birth, once almost universal, has become practically extinct. There's a slow comeback under way. In 1963 there were over 260,000 home births in England and Wales. By 1983 that had dropped to under 7,000. In 1993 there were more than 10,000.

Now I'm not quite an earth mother (I occasionally hanker after my waistline, will not believe in endorphins until someone produces one wriggling on a spatula for me, and reckon that three babies is quite enough), but I am a home birth keenie. So I'm going to go on about this at some length.

When my last baby was born, it was like Christmas. Our two children woke up in the morning to find that their sister had arrived while they slept. Without a rush to the hospital, without a sleepless night in a noisy ward, Beth was born at home. In our bedroom, on a plastic painting cloth belonging to her older brother and sister. And afterwards the whole family slept under one roof. And I shared a bed with my husband. Very alternative and radical.

At thirty-seven, knowing I was doing it for the last time and feeling confident that my body knew what it was doing, I wanted a home birth for my third baby. I had been born at home, after all, and so had my husband. I felt that having hospitals full of technology had made the medical profession overkeen to use it on everybody.

None of the doctors in our local practice would attend a home birth. But, as my community midwife – who used to do several a week before they dropped out of fashion – said, 'We don't need the doctors.'

My GP took the news quietly. 'I've given up hitting the roof,' she said. 'I think it's dangerous, but it's your decision.' Quite.

I had a routine pregnancy, like my others. Overdue by four days, I was summoned to the hospital for a check-up. There I met my first real obstruction to home birth in the shape of the registrar who examined me. 'A good sized baby, but not a ten-pounder this time,' he said. 'I see you want a home birth. Do you know what shoulder dystocia is?'

I did. It's when the baby's shoulders get stuck after the head is delivered and he can't expand his chest to breathe. I took a deep breath myself. Like many women, I have to fight the notion that doctor-daddy knows best. After all, I'd delivered two big babies and couldn't see a smaller one getting stuck. So I stuck to my guns.

But I nearly lost my home birth when the registrar took my blood pressure. It was high and I agreed to an induction in two days. At home I had a couple of glasses of wine, the community midwife came to check me and I didn't mention a slight backache I was scarcely aware of.

Then things started to get comical. Feeling rather peculiar I made rock cakes for the children's tea (see *Nesting*). I continued to ignore the backache. Since my first baby was twenty-one days late, my second twenty-two days late, at just four days over I hadn't even thought about getting out the cot linen. By the children's bathtime I knew it was labour. I felt the first contractions and made up the spare bed for my parents, who were coming to stay. A man knocked on the door selling tickets for the village harvest supper. I should have said, 'Please come back later. I'm having a baby just now.' But instead I rummaged about for change.

Upstairs I lay next to Jack to get him to sleep. Trouble was I couldn't lie still long enough. Then I sat up and my waters broke. Rosie, dependable as ever at bedtime, was fast asleep. Jack was wide awake and wanting to party. Specifically, he wanted to play shop-keepers at my bedside table. As I contracted, I bought imaginary apples and cups of tea – everything cost ninepence as always – and he dashed about shouting 'Keeper!'

At 9pm Jack finally went to sleep and we rang the hospital. I perched on the edge of my bed, not believing the urge I had to push. The midwife arrived and didn't even have time to put on her apron. Basically I'd been sitting on the baby's head for some time. As soon as I knelt on the painting cloth and leaned forward, Beth arrived. We all had hot drinks and rock cakes. Except for Beth.

No one in the family was excluded from Beth's arrival. My husband didn't have to go home and abandon me to the hospital for the night. I didn't have to leave the children and come home with an alien child. I like the woman-only clubbiness of the labour ward, but the sense of family at a home birth was overwhelmingly right. I could rest at home, whereas in hospital there was too much going on. It was bliss to be able to use my own loo. (See *Bowels*)

There were no injections, no drips, no huge crochet hook. Maternity wards in general hospitals are not likely to be infection-free. My two first babies between them had an eye infection, thrush and jaundice. Beth had nothing like that, and we hadn't even cleaned the paint off the cloth. Closeness was instant: there was no hospital routine to come between us.

But most births happen in hospital. My second birth was a very good advert for hospital birth. I had two super midwives, one of whom specialized in massage, and a comfortable labour room (sponsored by Marks & Spencer) with a huge beanbag. Hospitals have equipment as well as germs, and most of us these days feel safest there, at least for our first birth.

If you believe in endorphins, you may want to think twice about a drug-free hospital birth. Our natural reaction to hospitals is to produce adrenaline. Andrenaline kills endorphins.

You're not likely to get much sleep in a hospital. Crying babies, call buttons being pressed, new mothers coming onto the ward. With my first birth there was even a snoring husband across the ward, spending the night on two chairs, next to his snoring wife. Still, the sleeplessness is good training for the months ahead.

Home birth pack

The community midwife brings this round in a huge plastic bag in good time before your birth date. But it is not what you think: Mars bars, scented face wipes and champagne. It's drips, saline solution, syringes, huge pads for leaking undercarriages, and a gas-and-air cylinder without the mouthpiece.

Hormones

They're in charge here. Hormones run your menstruation, your pregnancy, your birth and breastfeeding. You're at their mercy. The only good thing about hormones is that you can blame them for all your bad behaviour while you're pregnant – whether it's eating gherkins with ice cream, being vile to your mother-in-law or crying over the Andrex puppy. Very handy.

Human chorionic gonadotrophin

This is the stuff that pregnancy tests detect. It's produced right at the beginning by the cells which later form the placenta. HCG is picked up even in the minutest quantities by those pee-on sticks. (See *Pregnancy kits*)

I *is for...*

Immunity

Immunity to *rubella* (German Measles) is important. It can handicap babies in the womb. Is it an urban myth that schoolgirls vaccinated in their teens have thought – with predictable results – they were being given immunity against pregnancy?

Incontinence

Yes, it can happen to you. Especially if you've had a long labour, a big baby, stitches and a catheter. Or any one of those. And no one ever talks about it. I cried when I realized I would have to remember to go to the loo because I couldn't feel the need. It does improve as the weeks pass, but long term the only solution is the turn-you-on pelvic floor exercises. It's not true that no one knows if you're doing them at the bus-stop – nobody is that cross-eyed and jut-jawed naturally – but it's better than wearing pads all your days. My midwife told me that more pads were sold for incontinence than menstruation these days. Bonuses gained from doing your pelvic floor exercises: less chance of a dropped womb when you're older, and orgasms, even at the bus stop. As they say, there'll be another one along in a minute. Cheaper and more reliable than buying *Cosmopolitan* in search of the Big O. (See *Pelvic floor*)

Induction

'Did they put a stick of dynamite up there?' asked the midwife as I lifted myself buttock by buttock onto the edge of the bed in the delivery room. You bet they had. The contractions had started out of a clear blue sky like the clappers. My fellow inductee was repeatedly shouting a terse command at her husband and any passing personnel, but in her state she can hardly have been in earnest about it.

Induction is when the medical profession reckons everyone – baby included – has been hanging round long enough and decides to speed things up. With your permission, of course. If labour hasn't started, they book you in and insert a prostaglandin pessary or squirt prostaglandin cream into the vagina – that's an artificial version of the stuff in men's sperm. Believe me, the natural thing is much more fun all round.

Prostaglandins ripen and soften the cervix. They also gets things going much more suddenly than in a normal labour. When I was induced because my second baby was twenty-two days over, I sent my husband home for lunch because nothing was happening. He left and I started a fresh chapter of the book I was reading. I never reached the end of the first page, because things suddenly got intense. I rang home, and then someone came along with that crochet hook again to break the waters, bring the head down and step the pressure up even more. In some labours a syntocin drip is used as well to get the contractions going. Induction is also used to speed up a labour which is going slowly. In all, it's worth running through the *Curry*, *Fun* and *Nipples* options first.

Internals

The sort of thing James Herriot was always doing to cows on *All Creatures Great and Small*. Not often used in antenatal care these days, but as soon as you're in hospital for the birth someone with a plastic glove is likely to come along and insert two or more fingers to see how dilated you are. And I mean dilated. Delighted does not apply, especially if you have a contraction while it's going on.

Intervention

One intervention leads to another in birth. So an epidural is often followed by syntocin, because you don't feel the need to push. A drip is always set up after an epidural in case blood pressure plummets. A catheter is likely too. An epidural also makes forceps more likely. An induction by prostaglandin is often followed by rupture of the membranes. But hey, you're not here to enjoy yourself, you're here to have a baby. . . .

Iron

Don't listen to anyone over fifty on the subject of iron in pregnancy – unless she's your doctor or midwife. Years ago everyone was put on iron tablets and got very constipated. They were also told to eat lots of liver, which women today should avoid because all the toxic nasties in the food chain concentrate in animals' livers. So eat your greens and hold back on the tablets until you're tested for anaemia at around twenty-six weeks.

J *is for...*

Jeans

Be realistic about jeans. After my first baby I flaunted myself in a pair of size twelves. After my second I stashed them in the back of the wardrobe. After my third I bought a pair of size fourteens. With an elasticated waist. The annoying thing is that jeans are ideal for mothers of young children, but it's the skinny kids in the shopping malls who can wear them best. With crop-tops, too.

You remember lying down on the bed when you were a teenager to pull up your jeans zip? You remember you had pelvic bones which stuck out and a concave stomach? You were that skinny kid once. Which means that she'll be the one buying the elasticated size fourteens one day. There's a kind of justice in that.

K *is for...*

Knickers

When I was first pregnant, I went to Marks & Spencer and bought seven pairs of their sensible, as-unsexy-as-you-can-imagine, waist-high knickers. I hadn't worn anything like them since school gym classes. Gradually, they rolled down the bump. Very uncomfortable. Bikinis which sling under the bump, whether maternity or roomy ordinary, that's what you need.

And, when you've had the baby, you need special net-type knickers to hold maternity pads in place. The blooming lovely phase is well and truly over. Other Pregnancy Books never show you floppy tummies in net knickers, do they?

Above all, you need the man to buy you something

lovely to wear when you're back to normal. Preferably in a generous size in case normal isn't quite what it was.

Knitting

You don't have to. That's what grandma is for. Not my mother, mind you. She started a matinée jacket when she was expecting my sister and finished it for me about four years later. If you feel some sort of need to knit, remember not to use pure wool. I knitted my little girl a sailor dress and she came up in bumps.

There are people who scoff at hand-knitted baby clothes, especially anything labelled matinée jacket. They smirk and say, 'How fifties!' This is because they have never tried to get a rigid little baby arm inside its clothes. You need soft things with lots of give, which granny's handknits have. And the 'skirt' part of the much maligned matinée keeps small legs warm when sitting in a baby chair. Babies and their grannies have been around much longer than designer totwear.

Ketones

'You're ketonic,' said the midwife at the hospital during my longest labour. By which she meant my glucose was down and I was producing ketones, acidic products of fat metabolism. Your body starts drawing on its fat because there's nothing in your stomach and labour slows down. Hence the idea of something like pasta in the early stages. Carbohydrate keeps you going longer. In most hospitals something like is the nearest you get. All those redundant school chefs found work in the hospitals, you know, and they toil away there in clouds of gravy browning and suet.

L *is for...*

Labour

It hurts, but it's inevitable and, unless you're going for the cut-out-and-keep variety, it's the only way you're going to get a baby. What is really annoying is the medical profession's tendency to get in on your act and decide what's happening. Labour, they reckon, doesn't start until three centimetres dilation, or until the contractions are coming every four minutes or so. Timing of established labour varies from hospital to hospital and fluctuates over the years.

But what about all that work before the medical fingers go in and the medical head is shaken? They put me down as having a twenty-one-hour first labour when I knew it was forty-two. I'd been there, drinking camomile tea and hugging an armchair in the small hours of yesterday. Any woman who has had a baby will tell you: labour starts when it starts hurting.

Labour is divided into three stages: first – until the cervix is fully dilated (ten centimetres); second – until the baby is born; third – until the placenta is delivered. Or: 'What do you mean, I'm only three centimetres? I've been here since last Tuesday'; 'I'm shivery and feel as if I need to go to the loo. Oh, my God . . . baby . . . baby'; 'What do you mean I can't ring my mother yet? It isn't over?'

Legs

Impossible to shave the outside of your legs towards the end of pregnancy, because of the bump. You have to go furry, treat yourself to a waxing or get your husband to do the job. The nice thing about legs in pregnancy is that, until your ankles go dropsical at the end, they remain recognizably yours – unlike other parts of your anatomy. So you can flash them about. And there's no rule which says pregnant women with good legs shouldn't wear short skirts. Wolf-whistlers are liable to tail off suddenly when you turn round, though.

Length of Pregnancy

It's 280 days or forty weeks and is counted from the first day of your last period, which is odd as that's probably fourteen days before you ovulated. But the baby doesn't have a calendar in there, so it's all rather academic. Ninety per cent of them arrive within ten days of the 280th day. (See *Due date*)

Ligaments

Hormones soften them up in preparation for labour. Sometimes they overdo it and things get too sloppy around the pelvis, hips and thighs. Some women end up like something from *Monty Python*'s Ministry of Silly Walks for a week or two until it sorts itself out.

Linea negra

This is the brown line which appears down your stomach when you start to bulge. Mine changed its course at the waist so it was an inch or so off to the right below my navel. It's caused by the muscles stretching.

I was mortified when expecting my third baby and chatting to a friend expecting her first. 'Look at this line,' she said. There it was – a firm dark line. I realized I hadn't got one this time. No line. Muscles already shot to hell. No more stretching to do. The stretched bits had just been hanging around waiting to be filled up by the next pregnancy. I thought about drawing my own *linea negra* with eyebrow pencil, as women did with stocking seams in the Second World War, when they had to go barelegged. But I'd never have kept my hand steady enough for long enough to cover the distance.

Not to be confused with the reddish line round the other side – a strange 'linea pinka' which extends from the anus between the buttocks while the cervix dilates during labour.

Lust

It doesn't go away. You just need more attention, more cossetting, and well, generally just more. . . .

M *is for...*

Maternity pads

No, those itsy bitsy panty liner things won't do. You need socking great, very long, very thick maternity pads – actually labelled 'Maternity Pads' – when you've had a baby. And you'll need to wear two at once at first. Hold back on the white bottom-hugging ski pants for a day or two. . . . You're a mother now. It's only decent.

Menstruation

You remember: PMT, periods, frisky middle of the month – the whole thing has been suspended for months. It comes back. Breastfeeding keeps it at bay for a while. If it's a very long while, better buy a pee-on pregnancy test. You ovulate before you bleed, and you may have been careless while believing you were carefree. (See *Contraception*)

Mid-term hots

There are women who only feel sexy when they're thin. If your libido soars in inverse proportion to your waistline, you may not believe in mid-term hots. But in the middle of your pregnancy, you'll probably start seducing your husband almost as often as he'd like. The tiredness and the sickness have gone. You're not worried about getting pregnant. And you're a sight thinner than you're going to be. As for that old advice about the missionary position being flattering to the stomach – you're now beyond all hope. Let your hormones rip and pin him down.

Midwives

'Midwife' means 'with the woman', and a midwife is all you need. Once you've been mid a man, of course! They all used to be trained nurses who chose midwifery as their speciality. These days they have 'direct entry'. In other words, the young ones don't know as much. Midwives can manage with very little sleep and have several mantras – 'quite normal', 'push' and 'relax'.

Doctors on labour wards always want to do something. Midwives know that there's a lot of waiting about in the job too. They see far more births than doctors and are far less likely to get worked up about it all.

The trouble with young midwives, apart from having waists which look as if they would snap if a pregnant women needed support, is that most of them

–71 –

haven't had babies. I didn't mind that with my second birth – at least one of us in the room had done it before, and the team of two midwives, including a trainee, provided a great support service.

But with the first one I was desperate by the beginning of the second day to talk to any woman who'd had a baby. The ward cleaner would have done, but I kept getting these slim girls with tiny waists. I felt like Babar the elephant. I wanted someone who knew from the inside what it was like – living, walking proof that you could go through all this and survive. Even walk normally again.

When a midwife who was also a mother arrived in the labour room, things improved and I produced the impossible – a baby.

After the birth midwives may do awful things like sticking needles into your baby, but they should be leant on for all they're worth – small waists or grandmotherly spread.

A community midwife will visit you for ten days after the birth. Don't try to impress her with home baking and a clean house. She'll put you down as a potential postnatal depression case straight away. Offer her instant coffee and a digestive biscuit or two, and get her to do difficult things like cutting your newborn's nails.

Some women get fed up with the intrusion of community midwives but I found them all wonderful – gossipy and reassuring – except for the one who decided to improve my breastfeeding technique with my first baby. She herself had never breastfed and left me with a pillow behind my back, a pillow under my elbow and a pillow under the baby. It was extremely hot and crowded.

Milk

It 'comes in', as they say, on the fourth day after the birth. It's okay – the baby doesn't need it any sooner. He or she is too busy knocking back the *Colostrum* (see earlier).

The baby and the breastmilk are designed for each other. Mucked-about-with cow's milk is second best. You feel I've already mentioned all this under *Breast-feeding*? You're quite right. And it crops up again under *Old farts*. I am a breastfeeding fan. So are babies.

It's a funny thing about breastfeeding. These days everyone eats everywhere. They chew gum and then throw it under your shoes. They sit next to you on trains eating disgusting things with onions hanging out of them. Chomp as you please is the rule. Unless, of course, you're a breastfed baby. Then you can only feed at home or hidden away, probably in a public loo.

The sight of a downy head under a T-shirt leads to glares, stares, mutterings and even expulsions from restaurants. In our country breasts are for calendars, rude magazines and pub jokes. Babies hardly get a look-in.

Britain has an appalling record on breastfeeding and lots of health problems among bottle-fed babies. There are medical advantages to breastfeeding – it reduces the risk of gastric and respiratory infections, among other things.

It's perfect, free and portable. No measuring, no sterilizing. No scrabbling about for equipment in the middle of the night. And, once you've got over the sore-ness of the first few days, breastfeeding is a pleasure. You get an enforced rest when you sit down or lie down with your baby.

And breastfed babies have much less pongy nappies. My husband finds them quite addictive, describing it as the whiff of new bread. There's another good reason – he's far more likely to change a breastfed baby's nappies.

I'm thinking of starting a breastfeeding equivalent to the Mile-High Club. (I've just had a thought: is that why airlines ban women once they're twenty-eight weeks' pregnant? Because anyone indulging in-flight in-loo entertainment *á deux* might get wedged in there?) Anyhow, my idea is a club for women who've breastfed in unlikely situations and places. I fed my third child while pedalling a pedalo on a French lake. Thank goodness my husband hadn't suggested windsurfing.

Miracle

'A little miracle,' Grandma will almost certainly say. This hyperbole may be justified in the case of the virgin birth. Otherwise, it's way out of order. Did Christ take nine months to turn the water into wine? He did not. Pregnancy and birth are much more mundane than miracles. And much harder work than a few thousand loaves and fishes.

Mirror

Believe it or not, there are some hospitals where they pass a hand mirror to you so you can see the baby's head emerging. It's rather like when the hairdresser shows you the back of your hairdo. You know that, if you run it under the tap for a minute when you get it home, it'll be fine.

Mobile epidural

The big E numbs your legs. Once that needle is in there, you can forget all notions of an active birth, and just enjoy the fact that the pain has gone. The mobile epidural is different. It doesn't block sensation. So, if you fancy strolling about, you can. You'll be aware of your contractions, but not of any pain. It's not yet available in all hospitals. You have to be careful not to be too energetic and cause yourself damage you won't feel until later. So don't indulge in too many squat thrusts.

Montgomery's tubercles

It sounds like something Monty should enter at the local fruit and vegetable show, but it's actually the name for those raised dots around the aureole of the nipple. More noticeable in some women than others. Perhaps they're there to help the baby grip, like studs on football boots.

Morning sickness

About half of pregnant women feel very sick or actually are sick, often (though not always) in the morning. It usually passes by the end of the third month. Eat little and often – a good excuse to nibble biscuits – and resolve never to get yourself in this condition again. Until the next time.

Mothers, his and yours

They vary. Mine is wonderful, of course. The worst sort is the rod-for-your-back variety. As in: 'Don't bring that baby into your bed. You're making a rod for your back,' and, 'Demand feeding? It's just a rod for your back.' Remember she probably left her baby down the bottom of the garden staring at the clouds for hours on end just because some child-rearing expert said it was a good idea. As for four-hourly feeds, ask her if she ever goes four hours without something to eat or drink. And whose baby is it anyway? On the other hand, they can be good to have around. . . .

Moving

It happens when pregnant. You look round your house and realize there's no way it will take a whole seven-pound infant without coming apart at the seams. You want to give him the country life/a bedroom of his own/the best primary school around, so you move. Enormous upheaval all round. The baby comes early. Probably because you helped to shift that teeny weeny wardrobe. You empty the last packing cases some time after the first term at primary school.

Mucous plug

Nature's equivalent to the tamper-evident bottle. It forms in the neck of the womb to keep it free of infection. When it comes away at the end of the pregnancy, it's called 'a show'. A curtain-up. The subsequent action is a real performance. Tickets non-transferable.

Mum

So you think you know who you are, where you're coming from, going to, etc? All that changes in the hospital.

It's not becoming a number that's so hard to swallow. It's becoming Mum, and being addressed in a strange version of the third person. As in: 'Now, if Mum could just put her feet in the stirrups, we'll check her stitches. Good. And how about Mum's bowels?'

Muscle tone

'You're actually carrying her very well,' said my GP with my first pregnancy. In other words, I hadn't done it before and my muscles hadn't been wrecked. By number three I felt I should be wearing a hoop round my neck and under my bump.

Muslin squares

Mysterious things, these are. They come in packs of twelve or so with diagrams of how to fold one to fit a baby's bottom. This is not what they are useful for. You need them to put over your shoulder in case your baby possets after feeding. Nice word, eh? Smelly problem. A young baby often brings up a little milk – the sphincter at the top of the stomach is rather weak – on your shoulder when you lift her. Some do, some don't. Milky shoulder decorations are all part of the battle of motherhood, but it's worth buying the squares to catch the worst. Bottoms need something altogether stouter.

N *is for...*

NAD

I spent ages trying to work out what NAD stood for when I saw it on my notes after an early antenatal inspection. It simply means 'nothing abnormal detected'. Actually, it was even written on my notes after a blood sample from my husband, having a tetanus check, was mixed up with mine. Whether SAD – something abnormal detected, man four months pregnant – appeared on his, I don't know.

Navel

At a certain point this will become your horizon as far as downward vision is concerned. You will see nothing below it. So, when the midwife asks you whether your feet have swollen, she might as well ask you whether you can see the far side of the moon. You're not even sure you have matching shoes on.

Children under three will get lost beneath your bump and you will be constantly walking on things left on the floor because you don't see them. When sitting down, your thighs will look remarkably short. If they're already short anyway, then you'll be amazed by how high your knees have suddenly become.

And then you will notice one other thing on your horizon. Your navel will have turned inside out, looking like a squashed cherry on a hillside. Handy for cleaning, but otherwise not an aesthetic improvement. After the baby, it goes back in, but remains roomy. None of this applies to people who are already outies, of course.

Nesting

This is one of the unofficial signs of labour. If the baby's due and you start painting walls, cleaning or baking, check your knickers for 'a show', your back for an ache and pack your bag for the hospital. You're feeling nesty. 'You must have been feeling nesty,' said the midwife who had just delivered my third baby, as she ate one of the rock cakes I'd made only a few hours before, when I had the teensiest nagging backache. . . .

Never again

We all say this. Usually more than once.

Nipples

They get big and dark with pregnancy. Towards the end they may ooze colostrum. They'll also be very sensitive, so tell that ugly brute of a partner to take his weight on his elbows. Certainly during your first pregnancy. After a few babies, the nipples will have moved significantly towards your armpits and it won't matter as much.

Nipple cream

Nipples get sore when you first breastfeed. (If they are sore for any length of time, get your midwife to check you have the baby latched on properly.) There are lots of nipple creams about. Most of them say you should wash the cream off before feeding the baby, which is a nuisance, especially if the baby is quite keen on being fed right now and is screaming the place down. Babies don't think: 'I'm getting hungry, I'll have something to eat soon.' They think: 'Hunger! Gimmee, gimmee! Now!' There's been research recently which suggests that some extreme food allergies in later life may even be caused by ingredients such as peanut products in nipple cream which the baby's immature system reacts to. On all counts an old-fashioned camomile cream like Kamillosan, which tastes nice and doesn't have to be washed off, is the best bet.

Nipple stimulation

Possibly should have come under the category *Fun* (see earlier), though as it's an in-labour stimulation, fun doesn't really come into it. If the contractions are slow, a hospital may well urge you to have a syntocin drip to speed things up. Nature's own syntocin is produced by gentle rubbing of the nipples. May be more use at home, either for a home birth or before going to hospital, as few partners would go in for stimulating their wives' nipples under the beady eyes of two midwives, a doctor and twelve students.

Noise

Once you are feeling quite strong movements from your baby, you may find that loud noises make her jump. I used to get on the train after work every night and find my womb leapt every time the train door slammed. It was an exhausting journey home. They do say that you can tell a little about your baby's personality from her behaviour in the womb. That jumping foetus grew into a highly alert baby, woken by the slightest movement or noise.

Talking of noise, if you're desperate to produce an Einstein without any delay, you may fancy one of those little clip-on sound boxes which play heartbeat sequences to the baby while in the womb. Early stimulation is the idea. Mozart next. Stimulation they call it. I would call it something else. . . .

O *is for...*

Obscenities

Some women have been known to utter these in labour, usually directed at the partner. As in, 'You * * * * ! Of course I want a * * * * ing epidural. I don't care what we agreed. It's not you * * * * ing well going through it. Tear up the * * * * * * * birth plan up, for * * * * 's sake. . . .' That sort of thing. Then the baby arrives and they become Virgin Mary pure of tongue.

Old bats

Old bats tell you stories. Horror stories about their births, other people's stretch-marks, birth defects, defects of the hospital you've chosen to have your baby in. Old bats ring up during those last few weeks at home when you're wondering what's going to hit you and tell you the worst possibilities. They live in hope that they will catch you just when you're recovering from a really gruesome experience. This is what an old bat sounds like:

'You haven't had it yet then? I expect you got your dates wrong. They'll induce soon and then you'll know about it. They induced my Sally – the consultant said she needed a stick of dynamite up there – and then [incomprehensible break for a snort of laughter] you should have seen the size of the forceps they used. Of course, they had to cut. . . . Then the shoulders got stuck. She'd had an epidural and didn't know what was going on until she raised her head and saw the doctor with one foot on the end of the bed literally hauling the baby out. . . .'

Old bats can upset you more than you think and deserve to be screened out by the answerphone or simply have the receiver put down on them. Do not worry about hurting them. They are very thick-skinned and will still ring up weeks later: 'Did you have forceps, then?'

Old farts

They lurk in cafés, pub gardens, hotel sitting-rooms and local parks – anywhere you may fancy sitting down with your baby to feed him. They tut-tut, they glare, some even 'have a word' with a waiter; others talk to each other about what you're doing in voices just louder than they need.

And old farts need not be old. The culture is so obsessed with breasts as sex and big as bad that even young people can be lacto-phobic. Ignore them all. Ask your baby what he thinks and take notice of that. Most women just feed under a T-shirt or jumper anyway. If you disrobe and fling off your bra and drip on the tablecloth, it's another matter, of course.

Old wives and their tales

Loads of old wives' tales relate to pregnancy. See *Bumps* and *Ring test*. Here are three of my favourites:

• Don't hang out the washing or hang curtains. The cord will wrap itself around the baby's neck. Worse still, you waste a damn good excuse for not doing tedious domestic tasks.

• If you overindulge your cravings, your child will have a birthmark. There was even an eighteenth-century claim of an oyster-mad woman who had a baby boy with black scurf on his hands, which looked just like the bivalve's shell. And reports abound of fruit fiends who have had babies with strawberry birthmarks, blackcurrant birthmarks, etc. Some have claimed the mark darkens in the fruit's ripening season.

• Then there's the tendency to blame a physical peculiarity on some fright the mother had in pregnancy. It's a belief ridiculed by Charles Dickens in *Martin Chuzzlewit*: 'Her husband's brother bein' six foot three, and marked with a mad bull in Wellington boots upon his left arm, on account of his precious mother havin' been worrited by one in a shoemaker's shop. . . .'

Other Pregnancy Books

There are three main varieties:

The straightforward medical job. You will know this by heart for your first baby. You will be able to say at exactly which day the eyelashes, toes and fingernails grow, when the baby first excretes, turns upside down, engages in the pelvis. It will fall open at the 'how your baby grows' pages.

The blooming book. You will recognize this by the pictures of calm, blooming mothers-to-be smiling up at their good-looking partners, or strolling through a field of cornflowers, or sitting on a pile of Heals fabric cushions, eyes closed, 'centering' themselves. Full of words like 'majestic', 'gravid' and 'ripe', it is bound to have a 'he's having a baby too' chapter. It will stay on the coffee table, covered in more and more magazines as the gap between you and the blooming ones widens.

The radical birth book. This is illustrated with strange little sketches of good positions for birth and pregnancy exercises. If there are photographs, most of them will be of the omigod variety – muzzy black-and-whites of babies' heads apparently emerging from bottoms, and blurred things going on in birthing pools. All rather real compared with the blooming book. Will probably contain lots of advice on baby massage, a consumer test of birthing pools and a rundown of aromatherapies for New Age labours.

Ovulation kits

If a female colleague emerges from the loo looking excited, makes a quick phone call and dashes home at lunchtime, she's trying to get pregnant and has just timed the all-important coitus using an ovulation kit. It tests your urine and tells you when you're fertile. Bad luck if it's in morning conference or on the bus.

P *is for...*

Partner

The term 'husband' is hopelessly loaded, judgmental and out of date. You didn't know that? In which politically incorrect bunker have you been hiding? If, like me, you have one of those old-fashioned married relationships, try to keep it a secret during the pregnancy business. The books, the antenatal classes and many of the hospitals have abolished husbands. They've been falling over themselves not to make people without them feel bad. There was a time when, out of politeness, all fathers-to-be were assumed to be husbands. Now they're all assumed to be partners. The word makes no gender assumptions either. So when Les Girls, both clad in dykey dungarees and only one with a bump, stagger into the labour room, there's no embarrassment. Partners all.

Paternity leave

Unless he irritates the life out of you, you'll need him around after the birth. He needs to learn about nappies, nipple cream and how often you'd like tea and toast served during the day. The trouble is, there's no legal entitlement to paternity leave in this country. It's up to the individual company and, although most large employers offer three to five days and some up to fifteen days, some offer nothing at all. Make sure the man finds out what's what and at least has holiday booked in around the date.

Pelvic floor

By the time the midwives, the health visitors and your GP have finished with you, you'll be sick of hearing about the pelvic floor. They start going on about it at antenatal classes and they finish six weeks after the birth with two fingers inside your vagina at the postnatal check, saying incredulously, 'Are you sure you're squeezing?' Then an intake of breath, a shake of the head, and, 'You'll have to do something about that or you'll be an incontinent old woman. Work those pelvic floor muscles.'

The pelvic floor is a muscle and tissue hammock slung across your pelvis. It has holes in it for urethra, anus and vagina, and so is parted and stretched as the baby is born. It also holds everything up, which is why a doctor who wants to threaten you with more than mere incontinence will also mutter darkly about 'a dropped womb' in later life. If they promised good sex rather earlier than that, the pelvic floors of the nation would be better exercised than they are.

Penis

There's an old joke – never told by men – about why some women find parking a car difficult. 'It's because,' splutters the teller, holding her finger and thumb about four inches apart, 'we're always being told this is six inches.' Mad giggles and nods all round. You'll be reminded of it in the sore days after giving birth. Spatial confusion takes over your brain every time a doctor or nurse mentions contraception. A ten-pound infant may have just slithered out of you, but you still can't believe you'll ever find a six-inch parking space again. Pillow talk after a birth is best summed up as: 'You want to put what where? It'll never fit.'

Piles

Pushing a baby out tends to push out everything else in the region too, including these little anal veins which add to the general riot of sensation in your undercarriage. Believe me, men know nothing. Anyhow, they subside after two or three weeks. Unlike the men, who are generally getting rampant by then. 'I have piles' is more likely to put them off than 'I have a headache'. Of course, you may not want to put them off, in which case, don't mention the piles.

Placenta

Tastes (so I'm told) rather like liver. Yes, some women do eat the organ which has nourished their baby via the umbilical cord for the last nine months. Some cook a little straight away, fried with onions, and pop the rest in the freezer for later. Apparently it's good casseroled with red wine and mushrooms – afterbirth *chasseur*, no less.

Others just put it to their lips raw. It's supposed to help the womb to contract, lessen bleeding and stabilize rioting hormones, preventing baby blues. It seems a lot for a pound or two of blood and tissue to do but many animals eat theirs, so who knows? In some cultures the mothers just bury the afterbirth instead. Most of us in the West let the hospital do whatever they want with it. Pre-AIDS a fair amount used to be sold to cosmetic companies for face creams.

You deliver the placenta in the third stage of labour either with the help of an injection of syntometrine or drug-free with a final push, perhaps with the midwife's hand against your stomach. Within about half an hour of the birth it slithers out and lands with a plop. Marbled purple, blue and pink, this remarkable link between mother and child is worth a good look before it meets its fate, whether *haute cuisine* or incinerator.

Politics

So you can't see anything political about having a baby? Men who usually wouldn't dream of laying a finger on you (or at least would only dream) pat the bump. Very gender political, that one. Then there's maternity leave and pay, the absence of tax relief on childcare and the whole thing about working mothers, single mothers and stay-at-home mothers. As for child benefit and nursery vouchers ... political awareness comes free with every pregnancy.

Postnatal elation

The labour was forty-two hours (my counting, not theirs). I had been through most of the midwives and most of the pain relief methods. My baby was perfect. My husband had crawled off home to bed at around 11pm. I should have slept. Instead I lay on the thirteenth floor of the hospital tower block, watching my first-born sleep, feeding her and gazing first at the moon and then at the rising sun, reflected in the sea less than half a mile away. I could no more have slept than done the splits. Incredulity and elation had done for me, as it did after the next, far easier birth. No one ever tells you that having babies makes you high. Plan plenty of sleep during the days – you may not have much chance at night – that follow the birth. Learn the art of feeding your baby while lying down. The only drawback is that you can't do it while having a glass of wine.

Pregnancy kits

These are expensive, addictive, very accurate and you can use them on the day you expect your period. If you have good eyesight, that is. The indicator, which responds to the presence of HCG (human chorionic gonadotrophin) in your urine, darkens as the days go by. Some of the pee-on tests include the command 'Don't splash the windows'. This is a bit disconcerting. But don't worry about your curtains. They're talking about the small and large windows on the test stick – one to give the result and one to show the test has worked. You can still buy older-style ones which involve peeing into containers and using dipsticks, but they're very messy and extremely difficult to use in the office loo. And you're bound to spill it on your shoe.

Pubs

Enjoy them while you may, because afterwards you may find you've got a narrower choice. Some pubs don't want children at all; some shove you out in the garden whatever the time of year; some have depressing family rooms with a broken activity cube on the floor and flock paper on the walls. But some now have children's certificates which mean families can go anywhere in the premises. I remember, before the certificate scheme was introduced, going into one pub with my brand new first baby, my husband and my parents, and being sent upstairs to the isolation room – a stale-smelling and empty place. Little milk-drinkers do strange things to some publicans.

Q is for...

Quickening

A lovely old-fashioned term for the movements of the baby in the womb, felt in a first pregnancy around sixteen weeks. It's often later with a second child because you're a baggy old thing by then and the baby can bounce about more without hitting the walls. The word 'quickening' carries connotations of life and it's much more accurate than the word 'kicking'.

Later on babies may kick and poke with elbows and knees, but first you feel something like popping in your womb, then stirrings and squirmings. There's nothing as violent or one-off as a kick. There are rolling movements in the middle of the pregnancy, while the baby still has space and has not settled down into her position for birth. Your whole belly will move visibly – fascinatingly for anyone who catches sight of the bumpy ripple travelling across your stomach.

As I lay in the bath one Saturday morning, pregnant with my older daughter, I put the soap on the flannel I had spread over my tummy and she nudged it off. My husband turned to look and she did it again. But usually babies are not so obliging. There's nothing more likely to send a baby into motionless stupor than a hand on a tummy waiting for a kick.

Towards the end of the pregnancy, movements are more restricted. Yours would be too if you were upside down with your head firmly held in a bone cage.

R *is for...*

Raspberry leaf tea

Vile tasting herbal brew supposed to make the womb contract. Recommended for late babies, only if *Curry* and *Fun* have failed. Buy it by the half ounce in your local healthfood shop and remember to sieve out the bits. Toe of frog and eye of newt may increase efficacy.

Reading

So, you used to do that, did you? Lie on the sofa with your nose in a book propped on your swelling tummy while you may. During maternity leave I worked my way through two thirds of *Teach Yourself Italian*. To be companionable my husband embarked on *Learn*

Russian, even brought the book with him into the delivery room. Once that baby arrived neither book was ever picked up again.

I have forgotten the grammar, but I still remember that '*la cuoca e una buon' amica del postino*'. Perhaps one day I will find out whether cook and postman ever consummated their love on the floury kitchen table as letters spilled everywhere. For birth number two I arrived with Anthony Burgess's *Nothing Like the Sun*, a biography of Shakespeare. I shut it as the contractions heightened and before the bard left school. He remains there, a permanent unwilling schoolboy.

Rectum

See *Piles*. And feel it pulling in if you're doing those pelvic floor exercises properly.

Ringing relations and friends

If you're having your baby in hospital, make sure your husband has coins for the phone box, so he can let your mother know all those rude words you said. Other people can wait until you get home, but she needs to know straight away that new mother and baby are doing fine. If only to stop her ringing up every ten minutes. Don't expect the nurses and midwives manning the reception desk to have change.

Ring test

Infallible way of telling the gender of the baby you are carrying. Thread your wedding ring (partner borrows a gold ring from someone) on a piece of cotton and hold over the bump. It goes round for a girl and to and fro for a boy. In fact, you'll find it does both by turns. The explanation is that it's telling you the gender in strict order of all the babies you have ever had and will have or may have, miscarriages included. Some people say it's round and round for a boy and to and fro for a girl. If you're having two of the same sex in succession, when does one stop and the next begin? Infallible, as I say.

S *is for...*

Scans

You'll have seen other women's scan pictures and wondered what all the fuss was about. You stare at a grey blobby thing while they enthusiastically point out baby elbows and nose. 'See that black bit there? That's its stomach.'

Sometimes you see a pretty clear spine and make the mistake of mentioning to the future mothers that it looks just like a kipper. Maybe, but now it's your kipper and there's never been such a beautiful one. Beware – your first scan of your first baby will absolutely knock you out.

When I was due for my first scan at fourteen weeks (although most first scans are now at eighteen weeks), the letter said: 'Drink 2/3 pints of water before you come.' At first I misread this as two-thirds of a pint, re-read it halfway down the drive and had to go back into the house to swallow as much as I could. I was only surprised not to be splashing the windows.

A quick dash to the hospital for a long wait with legs crossed, beside the glugging, swishing, spurting coffee machine. I remembered a friend who was waiting so long she had to go to the loo and got a rotten scan picture. 'Hang on, hang on,' said a nurse encouragingly. 'You won't feel the pressure when you're lying down.'

I know this is a lot about bladders for one entry. But bladders are big – in a manner of speaking – when you're pregnant. They wake you up before a baby and are never the same after a baby. When you're pregnant whole areas of your body which have been of only – um – passing interest to you, suddenly become study areas for the medical profession. The bladder is high on the list.

Eventually I was lying on a bed while a radiographer ran a cold metal something over my jellied stomach. My husband was standing at the end of the bed. I couldn't help thinking of my father's comment that it seemed a 'bit of a cheek to be spying on the baby', but couldn't actually believe I'd see anything which looked like a baby anyway.

On the screen next to me a grey mass cleared and the shape of a tiny baby appeared. I wasn't expecting that. I was expecting a blob or a kipper, a tadpoley thing at best. Instead there was a proper baby with tiny pulsating heart, a stomach, a clear spine. It was a mini-baby, all of four and a half inches long, and it moved around. An arm was flung out in welcome. There was a sort of hiccough and a bobbing around. There was a tiny clenched fist, dark lines showing the division between the fingers. I was surprised by my tears and my husband held my foot.

'Looks like a perfectly formed baby,' said the radiographer. And I thought: 'Of course, an exceptional specimen – naturally.' I suppose that's what my mother would call the 'They're all marching out of step except our Tommy' syndrome – maternal blindness. Later David claimed she merely meant the mini-baby looked normal, not the nonpareil in the four-and-a-half-inch class.

A scan is a picture produced by ultrasound (high frequency we can't hear) bounced off the baby in the womb. It is used to check just how pregnant you are, to pick up possible defects and to ascertain the position of the foetus and placenta. A diagnostic tool to the medical profession, an amazingly wonderful thing to the prospective parent, it is now used routinely. It seems to have no side effects but hasn't been going for long enough for this to be known for certain.

Sense of smell

If you suddenly find you've got a sense of smell like a bloodhound, you could be pregnant. No doubt nature's way of sniffing out unfaithful partners and ensuring father stays with his young family.

Other women find they can't smell a damn thing because their noses are blocked when pregnant. Nature's way of helping women with smelly partners stay with them for the sake of the young family? It's caused by the swelling of the linings in the nose and sinuses. Unlucky women find their nose blocks up before they've even missed a period and stays blocked for the duration.

A friend of mine became bonded to her Sinex spray through the last three months of her pregnancy. She raised hell when the midwife took it away from her in labour. Her contractions slowed right down until she got it back.

Sex

It's all a bit weird, doing it when there's someone in there. Having sex in a caravan must be like this. You feel half watched. Sure, there's a flimsy screen door, a mucous plug in the neck of the womb. But that rocking to and fro must be a dead give-away.

As the months go by, it gets more and more difficult for the chap, keeping his weight off the bump as best he can, to reach the vital bits. Some couples become very resourceful and gymnastic about the whole thing, assuming all sorts of Olga Korbutt contortions so as not to miss any pleasure. If you find yourself in a truly ridiculous position, maintain a committed and serious outlook. Giggles will result in wounded male pride and collapse of stout party (you).

Shaving

An antiquated torture for pregnant women on admission to hospital. You don't hear of it now, so presumably it has died out. I can't imagine much worse than having to cope with pubic stubble just after having a baby.

Shopping

You've heard of shop 'til you drop. Well, when you're pregnant, it's shop 'til you pop. You could buy some absolutely-vital-impossible-to-live-without piece of baby equipment every week of your pregnancy and still have a gift list for grandma. There are cot-bumpers, baby swings, big lacy frocks for Moses baskets, changing tables, mobiles with twenty different surfaces to stimulate your baby, tone pagers so your partner doesn't miss the birth. You could spend thousands. Or you could buy some baby clothes, nappies, a car seat and a few other things, and call it a day. And just think: Jane Austen didn't have ABC cotbumpers or A is for Apple wallpaper borders. Don't fall for the old superstition about not buying things for the baby until after the birth. You may have a shopping-list-literate partner, but if not just think what a total mess he will probably make of the whole thing, especially if he's exhausted after going through the labour. Buy the basics while you can still enjoy going round the shops. Don't go mad – just a few things to put in a hospital bag for you and the baby, and a few spares ready at home. It's worth buying a bottle and some ready-made formula milk in case you're tired and need a break for a night. If you've got some ready in the fridge, your partner can feed the baby while you sleep. And don't buy nappies in just new-born size. If your baby is much over eight pounds, they won't be big enough. Some maternity units have baby shops.

Show

The mucous plug comes away in a blood-streaked 'show' when labour is due. It's nothing dramatic, but is often the first sign that things are under-way.

Sink

After around seven months your partner will have to do all the washing-up. It's worth a try, anyhow. The bump hits the edge of the sink and you have to lean forward at a bad-for-your-back angle, which is incredibly uncomfortable and gives you a very wet tummy.

Sleep

Get as much sleep as you can. Have as many weekend lie-ins as you can. As much noisy sex as you can. Once the baby has arrived, you'll have little of the first and none of the second. It's awful. Becoming one of those self-satisfied people who get up at dawn and talk about it as 'the best part of the day' is small consolation for the loss of breakfast in bed, newspapers in bed, man in bed.

Smell

Warm and sweet. Partners reckon pregnant women smell marvellous. They usually reckon this in bed just when you're thinking about going to the loo, about the agonizing cramp in your right calf or simply about sleeping. They start sniffing you and licking you, and in the end you'd be less molested sharing a basket with the dog.

So what?

There's a state of mind which affects lottery winners. It goes something like this: 'We've won £14m. So what? It won't change our lives.' It's not true, of course. Having three homes, a Rolex for every day of the year and a personal trainer cannot be mistaken for having a terrace, a Swatch and membership of the local gym. Pregnant couples often pretend they are lottery winners. 'We're pregnant,' they say. 'So what? It won't change a thing.' Oh yes it will. Some realize it straightaway (something to do with trying to perch a rubber ring for piles on a wine bar stool?) and others take a while. The truth is that small babies are very portable. Mine have between them been to parties, conferences and interviews. But there is no similarity between being able to go anywhere any time and having to take with you an utterly dependent, unreliable and exhausting little creature which leaks. No similarity at all. If you find yourself saying, 'So what?', don't watch the faces of your childless friends. Check out the older, wiser eavesdropper. You'll recognize her. She's the one smiling and shaking her head. And, for once, it's not the gin.

Stitches

One of the many things mothers don't tell daughters about having babies. Sometimes you split. And, if you split once, the chances are you'll probably split again. Some claim you can avoid it by rubbing almond oil into the perineum in the later stages of pregnancy. They don't tell you how to reach the perineum in later stages of pregnancy. Or what effect it has on your partner when you roll into bed smelling of marzipan. If you do have stitches from either a tear or a cut (episiotomy), Witch Hazel does wonders for the bruising. That's not an *Old bat*, but a clear liquid available cheaply at any chemist. Also you could buy a blow-up rubber ring to sit on – so chic.

Stopwatch

Useful for timing the contractions before going to hospital. You've probably been told to ring up the labour ward when they're five minutes apart and go in when three minutes apart. Some labour wards even want to know how long they're lasting. Make sure your partner knows how a stopwatch works. For my first birth my husband timed my contractions exactly and we set off for the hospital when they were three minutes apart. Sadly, by the time we got there, they'd slowed down so much the midwives nearly sent us back home. Third time round it was a home birth. The stopwatch went funny. Contractions were fast and furious by the time we sent for the midwife. The stopwatch just kept dinging. An egg-timer would have been better.

Stretch-marks

'She woke up the other morning and they were all over her, from her neck to her knees,' one woman was telling another in ooh-aah tones at the antenatal clinic I went to. Soldier ants? Purple warts? No, stretch-marks. They're reddish streaks on your breasts and stomach caused by the stretching of the skin. You get them early on your breasts, because they enlarge quite soon. The marks fade to silver after the birth, but rarely go entirely. Vitamin E oil may help them fade. Some people are prone to them, others not. They were no problem to me: I had them before getting pregnant. Years of yo-yo dieting gave me silver streaks well in advance.

Swimming

Wonderful thing to do when pregnant: you feel weightless. You'll need a maternity swimsuit. The choice which faced me was plain navy, plain black or bright yellow daisies. Why try to hide the bump behind fat lady fashions? Why be ashamed to shine? I chose the daisies and undulated about the local pool, mainly during the women-only sessions, looking like a moving meadow. If there's a sign above the maternity swimsuits which says something like 'Buy your ordinary size', don't believe it. The manufacturer's idea of making allowance for the bump is a tuck here, a bit of ruching there. What you need is extra fabric, feet of it, fetchingly folded about your middle. Wise up, size up and try it on first.

T

is for...

Talking down

'If baby does a poo inside Mum's tum . . .' This is the
way some people talk to pregnant women, especially at
the antenatal classes, where you're treated as if it were
the local infant reception class. Some women swear
they've had midwives refer to their 'furry front bottom'.
As soon as you're pregnant it's assumed that your brain
shrinks as your womb expands. The babytalk tends to
come from the nursing (mainly female) side. Something about dealing with what they euphemistically
call 'down there' brings out the 'dicky birds' and 'gee-
gees' in their vocabulary.

The doctors, registrars, consultants etc (mainly
male) have a different technique. The older ones tend

to behave like your daddy. They are in charge. You are there to receive their wisdom and do as you're told. The younger ones are actually rather frightened of finding an intelligent woman on their hands and they tend to be as silent and grand as possible, using medical terminology only. Ask questions and refuse to be cowed. Look at them and smile. Warm 'em up.

Tampons

Don't even think about using these puny things for your post-baby bleed. And remember – you'll need a big size when things get back to normal afterwards. (See *Blood* and *Maternity pads*)

TENS Machine

My friend - the fish and chips in labour one - was most enthusiastic about this method of pain relief. 'It's all you'll need,' she told me. She lied. What she meant was that it was all *she* needed. I needed a bottle of brandy, a knock over the head and a morphine drip. TENS stands for 'transcutaneous electrical nerve stimulation'. It's a little black box that you hold. Wires leading from it are taped to your back. Four electrodes scramble the pain messages to the brain. You operate it yourself with each contraction. Frankly, it did nothing for me, but other people are so keen they hire a machine beforehand so they can use it at home during the early part of the labour.

Thank you

Saying thank you can wait. I nearly went insane worrying about thanking people for all the flowers I had when my first baby was born. I worked in the sort of office where flowers were sent all the time – mainly oh-so-tasteful all-white arrangements from very posh florists. The senders asked a secretary to make a phone call. Unfortunately I didn't have a secretary on hand to find pen and paper, feed the baby, be examined when the community midwife called, make me actually eat and drink something during the day, and put in a few hours sleep for me. It's mayhem for a while after a baby.

Thin people

Avoid them while pregnant. Or adopt a lofty attitude. After all, you are blooming, ripe, fulfilled, etc. They are on Slimfast. One thing I really enjoyed was meeting an equally hugely pregnant friend for lunch and then strolling side by side in majesty around the shopping centre afterwards. Being in pairs helps enormously. You tend to think: what a lot of odd skinny people. How flat they are!

Things

Let's be realistic about this. When you go into hospital to have a baby, you don't need many things – just enough for you and the baby for a couple of days. If you're in for longer, your husband (if equipped with compass and diagrams of drawers and airing cupboard) can bring extra supplies. What you don't need would probably make a longer list. You don't need a load of books and magazines. If you're being induced, you may need something to read until the contractions get going. If you're already a few centimetres dilated with regular contractions, there's no way you'll be able to read much more than a bus ticket before you have to breathe out, press a button on your TENS machine or take a gulp of gas and air. And after the baby is born, time moves several times faster than normal. Reading, cross-stitch or whatever you've brought is not going to get a look in. By the time you've changed her, filled in a form, fed her and changed her again, it'll be lunchtime. For her, at least.

Three-in-a-bed

Troilism is almost inevitable after you've had a baby. Not in the search for some new sex sensation, but in the search for some sleep. Baby can feed while you doze if you bring her in with you. Buy a big bed now.

Tiredness

Nature's way of preparing you for all those sleepless nights. The first three months are the worst. It's a tiredness you've never felt before. You'll find you can sleep for hours and hours more than normal. Your partner will become quite depressed because you fall asleep as soon as your head hits the pillow. He's thinking of nine sexless months. But the exhaustion does disappear around fourteen weeks. Then it's heigh-ho for several months of contraception-free sex, but see *Contraception*.

Transition

The contractions are at their strongest and fastest, then suddenly they ease off and you may feel slightly cold and shivery. This is transition, the shift from stage one to stage two in labour. The final opening of the cervix is happening, and the body is posed for the expulsive contractions which will bring the baby down. When the contractions do come now, they make you feel like pushing. If the midwife says wait, it's a breathing space to gather your strength for the second stage. Some women actually feel sleepy during transition. Others feels irritable, especially if they are stuck there for a while. Partners should be tactful in a first birth – they may be savaged. Women who've been this way before feel a sense of achievement and relief. Can't be long now and it's all downhill. A good time to manoeuvre yourself into a different position to help the slithery one to slither.

Truth

An early casualty in the pregnancy stakes. No one tells you what it's really like to be pregnant or to give birth. Mothers and friends don't want to put you off. *Old bats* (see earlier) want to tell you, and to hear, only the bad bits. On top of that it's different for everyone. Meantime, this book is the nearest thing you're likely to get.

U
is for...

Ululations

In labour some people use breathing techniques, some blow, some rock to and fro, some swear. And some ululate. That is, they howl. When you're pregnant, some-one - most likely a man - will say to you, 'Of course, in the African state of Hellhole, women just go off into the scrub and squat to give birth. No fuss, no drugs, just a bit of grunting and howling. They strap their babies on their backs and get back to work the same afternoon. We're too sophisticated.' Yes, too sophisticated to be dead at forty. Ululate in his ear and warn his partner that she's shacked up with a barbarian, who will be despotic with her birth plan, and probably be sick long before it's time to squat.

Unbelievable

The things you wouldn't credit about pregnancy:

• It can make your face change colour. It's called chloasma or the mask of pregnancy. The hormones affect the skin pigment and you can get dark patches on your face.

• An ache in your shoulder may be the first sign - if you notice it - that you are pregnant.

• The clitoris becomes very sensitive.

• The cell formed by the fusion of sperm and egg is smaller than a pinpoint.

• Men at the office suddenly become intimate with your stomach. They comment on it and pat it.

• Darkness helps in the labour room. It's said to encourage the endorphins, the body's natural painkillers.

• You sweat more because your metabolic rate increases.

• Some babies start sucking their thumbs in the womb.

Undercarriage

Private parts? More like privates on parade. Good God, by the end of the whole thing you'll probably end up on your back, feet in stirrups while a total stranger practises her embroidery on you.

Urine

Everybody will be terribly interested in this through-out. It will be collected, sent off to labs and tested with little indicator sticks. Probably sniffed and tasted, too, I wouldn't wonder. What they're looking for is sugar and protein. They more often find garlic and Chardonnay. (See *Bladder*)

V *is for...*

Vagina

This is where it starts and finishes. That's about the size of it. And its size is amazingly different at the beginning and the end. Latin for 'sheath', but presumably you weren't using one of those.

Varicose veins

Nasty things. Insist on a low stool for under your desk at work and put your feet up as much as possible at home. Otherwise it's old lady support tights - yuck.

Vasectomy

Once you've had your babies, this is the best and the most reliable way to have safe, spontaneous lovemaking.

So why won't more of the beggars get it done, eh? You've just had months of fingers, speculums, monitors, forceps, babies' heads, scalpels, needles and thread around your bits. And the thought of one tiny little snip sends them stratospheric. There are subtle ways of persuading them, such as a sex strike. On no account allow them to talk to a friend who's had it done and will describe the pain plus outsized balls for a week afterwards.

Vegetables

Eat a lot of veg to keep things moving just before the birth. And keep some raw cabbage leaves in the fridge afterwards. If your breasts become engorged (painfully overfull) when the milk comes in, very cold cabbage leaves inside your bra will help. It's a sight better than most recipes for cabbage anyway.

Ventouse/vacuum extraction

The continental alternative to forceps, now routinely available over here. May give your baby a pointy head for a day or two, but much less sore for both of you than the old salad tongs. Baby is basically sucked out with a cap and vacuum when he gets stuck. Looks like an Enid Blyton pixie. May be preferable to the usual Winston Churchill effect.

Visitors

When you've just had a baby it's important for visitors to come, but it's even more important for them to go away. Have a pact with your partner that he will take them on one side and say: 'Actually, she gets really tired. . . .' If they come and make vague offers of help, take them up on it. Washing up, tidying - anything you can get someone else to do – means that you'll be less tired and worried, and more able to curl up with the baby and sleep.

Stock up on flower vases before the birth.

W

is for...

Water

It might sting when you pee after stitches. Pour warm water over your genitals at the same time to ease things.

Water birth

Yep, it's not enough being in labour. Some women want to be in water as well. Possible at home - as long as your floor can take the weight of a full birthing pool - or in a hospital. Trendy but effective way of lessening the pain. Controversial because some doctors reckon being born into what may well be dirty water - even if the midwife is ready with a pooper-scooper - is not a good thing. But there's been little lasting heavyweight opposition to the trend, which began in 1982 with a BBC television programme on obstetrician Michel Odent's birth room with pool at Pithiviers in France.

Many mothers think it's wonderful. A friend of mine had her fifth baby in water after four land births and a seven-year gap. It was by far the best of the lot, she said, even though the baby was more than eleven pounds.

The water lessens the pain of the contractions - or at least your perception of the pain - and makes moving about a lot easier. It lessens the effect of gravity, though, and most women leave the pool for the actual delivery. But some of those who think they're only there for the first stage are surprised by how right it feels, refuse to get out and deliver into the water.

A birthing pool gives a woman a certain sense of privacy. She has her own environment. And precious few doctors are likely to invade it.

Waters

Or amniotic fluid. Amazing facts about the liquid your baby floats about in: it's full of nutrients; the baby inhales it, exhales it; swallows it and pees it; it's constantly being replenished; at the time of the labour there'll probably be about a pint and half in there. But not for long: it'll soon be over your mattress. That's if you're lucky and not shopping at the time, of course. A brilliant way of getting to use the staff loo in shops which don't have any for customers is to scream that your waters are about to break.

Weekends away

Whether it's bed and breakfast or posh hotels, do lots of it before you have a family. Spontaneous upping and going is much harder when you have to think of travel cots, backpacks, and how a toddler will behave going round that fascinating country church or into that charming country restaurant.

Weight

You're supposed to put it on. A normal weight gain is between twenty-two pounds and thirty pounds, though some women put on as little as sixteen pounds and some as much as sixty-four pounds. The good thing is that most hospitals weigh in kilogrammes so there's no real need for you ever to know just how much you've put on. It's unbelievable that something weighing seven pounds or so can do this to you.

Willie

What you're looking for on the scan so you can tell whether you've got a boy or a girl. But babies adopt all sorts of demure poses in the womb once the flashbulbs start popping and there's often no way of telling. If you do see something, it's probably a bit of umbilical cord. The radiographer may tell you what gender it's likely to be - if she can see it herself - but only if you live in an area without cultural tendencies to do away with female babies.

Woof-woof

This is what the baby's heartbeat sounds like on the doctor's listening device - a sonic aid about as big as a small cassette player. It works by ultrasound and plays out. Great thing to hear. Later on the heartbeat is stronger and they use just a trumpet, keeping the woof-woof to themselves. It saves on the batteries, but how mean can you get?

Work

People become very heated about mothers who work and mothers who don't. Get to grips with maternity law and your own employer's maternity policy before you tell anyone at work that you're pregnant. Keep your options open. Your decision will depend on your own desires, your mortgage and the National Lottery.

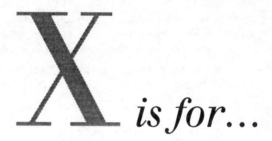

X *is for...*

X is for kisses.

You need lots all over your rounding stomach. Make sure your partner reads this page and daily follows it to the letter.

XXXXXXXXXXXXXXXXXXXXXXXXXXXXXXXXXXXXXXXXXXXXXXXX
XXXXXXXXXXXXXXXXXXXXXXXXXXXXXXXXXXXXXXXXXXXXXXXX
XXXXXXXXXXXXXXXXXXXXXXXXXXXXXXXXXXXXXXXXXXXXXXXX
XXXXXXXXXXXXXXXXXXXXXXXXXXXXXXXXXXXXXXXXXXXXXXXX
XXXXXXXXXXXXXXXXXXXXXXXXXXXXXXXXXXXXXXXXXXXXXXXX
XXXXXXXXXXXXXXXXXXXXXXXXXXXXXXXXXXXXXXXXXXXXXXXX
XXXXXXXXXXXXXXXXXXXXXXXXXXXXXXXXXXXXXXXXXXXXXXXX
XXXXXXXXXXXXXXXXXXXXXXXXXXXXXXXXXXXXXXXXXXXXXXXX
XXXXXXXXXXXXXXXXXXXXXXXXXXXXXXXXXXXXXXXXXXXXXXXX
XXXXXXXXXXXXXXXXXXXXXXXXXXXXXXXXXXXXXXXXXXXXXXXX
XXXXXXXXXXXXXXXXXXXXXXXXXXXXXXXXXXXXXXXXXXXXXXXX

Y *is for...*

Yoga

The trouble is that most of us couldn't get into a yoga position even when not expecting a baby. But practised yogis claim it helps with pregnancy and birth. Tailor sitting (soles of the feet together and knees as low as you can get them) and squatting like one of those chubby little Indian statues all help to stretch the perineum and the pelvic floor muscles. And the trance-like breathing helps you to stay calm. Not to be recommended late in the pregnancy if you don't know what you're doing. It would be very embarrassing to get knotted up and have to call for the fire brigade as well as a midwife.

Yoni

A Hindu word for the vagina as an object of veneration. I thought you might like to know that.

Yours

After all the build-up, the fuss, the medical supervision and the advice, the baby is yours. Yours to take away from hospital and look after. No tests, no licences, no arrow saying 'This way up'. Terrifying.

Z *is for...*

Zygote

A germ cell resulting from two fused reproductive cells. Which is where all this began. Fun, wasn't it?